David Brown Tractors

1936 - 1964

FARM CLASSICS
Volume One

Alan Earnshaw

NOSTALGIA ROAD

CONTENTS

Is published jointly by
Atlantic Transport Publishers
Trevithick House
West End, Penryn
Cornwall, TR10 8HE
Tel. 01326 373656 Fax. 01326 378309
&
Trans Pennine Publishing
PO Box 10
Appleby-in-Westmorland
Cumbria, CA16 6FA
Tel. 017683 51053 Fax. 017683 53558

Layout & Design
Kevin Bradley
Burwain Studios, Penrith

Reprographics
Barnabus Design & Repro
Threemilestone, Truro,
Cornwall, TR4 9AN

and printed in Huddersfield by
The Amadeus Press
Leeds Road

© TEXT: Alan Earnshaw 1997; Photographs: David Browns (Unless Credited Otherwise)

Cover pictures:
FRONT: *Trackmaster 50 and Klaus combine in 1952*
REAR TOP: *880 and 990 models at the Smithfield Show in 1963.*
REAR BOTTOM: *The first Oliver tractor to come off the assembly line is driven by David Brown junior and watched by senior managers.*
TITLE PAGE: *David Brown drives a model 25C at the Harrogate Convention in 1953.*
THIS PAGE: *Royal Agricultural Society Show 1952.*

British Cataloguing in Publication Data
A catalogue record for this book is available from the British Library

David Brown Tractors 1936 - 1964

The story of the David Brown tractor is one of the most fascinating pieces of British agricultural engineering history, and it began over six decades ago in the heart of the British wool textile industry, the West Riding of Yorkshire. How tractors came to be built in Huddersfield, more famous for worsted cloth, a fine choral society and its football team, is a story which we will recall in due course. But at the outset it is important to say that the firm of David Brown are still an important employer in the town, and the company's Park Gear Works are to host the launch of this book on 9th May 1997. This is just a small part of their continuing support to my research, and it is with grateful thanks that I acknowledge the vital contribution that my former employers have made towards this book. It is also important to acknowledge that this publication is not just down to my solitary endeavour. Indeed, this is the work of many hands and a combination of the personal recollection of many people who were deeply involved with the family firm of David Brown. From shop-floor engineers, through middle-management, to the higher-echelon of the company board room, recollections and memories have flowed to make this book the first authentic work on the history and products of David Brown Tractors Ltd. In its writing I am especially indebted to the invaluable assistance rendered by the former David Brown Tractor personnel; Herbert E. Ashfield, Albert Berry, Anthony Heath, Thomas Lazenby, Leonard Craven, Ron Fisher, John Hudson, Bob Marsh and Derek Marshall. From non-DBT personnel, may I thank Adam Brown (President of the David Brown Tractor Club), Messrs. Gibbs of Bedfont, Robin Kedward, Messrs Rickerby & Co., Mike Smart, Bill Smith, Bob Thomas, Alec Winspear and the many other DB enthusiasts, farmers and sales-people who have supported this book. For my own part, I have had the great pleasure of bringing together the recollections of those involved, and had the pleasant delight of reliving many fond memories.

From infancy David Brown Tractors were a close part of my life, they had to be because we lived right opposite 'A Block' of the Meltham Mills works. When I was old enough to go to school, I walked down Meltham Mills Road past the huge red-brick building known as 'C Block' into the local primary school which was located directly opposite 'E Block'. Yet despite the enormous size and complexity of Meltham Mills works (pictured inset), this was essentially a rural village and the works fitted snugly into an attractive and deeply wooded valley on the edge of the Pennines. It was an unlikely setting for any large engineering works, but here thousands of tractors were produced between 1939 and 1988. Meltham Mills and the nearby town of Meltham were dominated by the influences of this engineering giant and this exacting, but rather benevolent company, touched the lives of thousands of local folk. To work at David Brown's was to be part of a large family, and by extension this family arrangement pervaded outwards from the works into the surrounding districts. For local lads, the reward for completing our education with good grades meant, it seemed, a job for life. I joined the David Brown Corporation as a Commercial Apprentice at the end of the 'swinging sixties' when the company was at its Zenith, flower power was all the rage and I had much longer hair than I have today.

By this time the firm had grown from very humble beginnings, just over a century earlier, when the first David Brown started small wooden gear-making shop in Huddersfield. From its inception in 1860 the company expanded from employing a handful of people to 16,000 just over a century later. By this time the firm had become an international operation with a turn-over in excess of £55 million and had won the Queen's Award to Industry. For its first four decades David Brown specialised in the production of wooden patterns for firms who were casting gears for local textile machinery manufacturers. However, as technology progressed these manufacturers began to require more advanced gearing systems for drive delivery; Brown's saw the opportunity and exploited it. An early innovation was the change from cast-iron to steel, as the demands on gearing systems grew. By the end of the 19th century, Frank Brown, son of the founder, decided that the firm's Huddersfield premises were much too small for their needs, and a lengthy search was instituted for a new factory. After failing to acquire a site at Gledholt, alongside the Huddersfield to Manchester railway, Brown looked around for another site

where rail access was available. Thanks to a business acquaintance, William Whiteley, the firm purchased a large country residence, Park House at Lockwood, which was adjacent to the Huddersfield - Sheffield railway. Manufacturing was commenced in the grounds, and the birth of the world famous Park Gear Works (Pictured Above) had begun.

After a period of considerable consolidation, aided by a full order book through the First World War, the firm began to expand on its gear manufacturing activities. In this period Brown's devised and patented the precision worm reduction gear. In the 1920s further developments were made to the precision products range, and the company began to achieve a monopoly in supplying gearboxes to the developing automotive trade - particularly motor lorries and buses. Having successfully survived the Depression, they were able to acquire the properties of other companies which had not been so lucky. It was Frank's son, David (Pictured Inset c.1952), who took the initiative, first of all by purchasing the old Cammell Laird Tyre Rolling mill at Penistone in 1934. Located approximately 12 miles south of the firm's Lockwood headquarters (and also situated on the same railway line), the plant was converted into a steel foundry reducing the need to purchase raw supplies from outside sources.

The second David Brown was very often at odds with his father, but the grandson of the founder showed tremendous innovative flair, and it was his drive that moved the company forward to its international status. For

example, although the company had already been unsuccessful in its attempts to join the motor manufacturing industry, David soon began to realise the tremendous potential which vehicle manufacturing could provide. When an Irish engineer by the name of Harry Ferguson approached the company to help with his ideas for a new farm tractor, David Brown seized the opportunity. Ferguson came from a farming background, but at an early age he left the farm and became an automobile mechanic. He soon became well-known in his locality, due to his exploits with motor-cycles and racing cars, but he went on to form his own company repairing tractors, most of which were of American origin. He was a very individual character, and quite unlike David Brown but the two of them formed a partnership in 1936; between them they produced the first tractor in the world to be equipped with hydraulic lift and three-point linkage. Sadly the partnership was not harmonious, and it is easily understandable why two extremely capable engineers with completely different (but strong) temperaments should, in the long run, each seek to go their own way. Ferguson's story is another matter, but Brown was adamant that he could and would produce tractors that were both innovative and revolutionary. He saw, all too clearly, the massive changes that were coming in British agriculture. Technical revolutions were always welcomed with open arms, particularly in times of war, and already the storm clouds were growing over Berlin. David and Frank argued over the practicality of the plan, to the extent that the father refused his son the much needed manufacturing space at Lockwood. However, as the Munich crisis developed, David Brown began acquiring the vacant Meltham Mills which were located some three miles from Lockwood, also benefited from being connected with a branch line railway. These cotton thread mills had been run down from 1934 onwards, after the Depression forced the United Thread Mills to transfer their production from Yorkshire to Scotland. The thread company were desperate for a buyer, the local people were desperate for work - Brown got the plant for a song. He well knew from discussions he had already had with the Ministries of War, Supply and Food Production, that every inch of engineering space would be welcomed in the very near future. Throughout the war Meltham Mills played a vital role in war production, with tank gearboxes, aero-gears and military tractors being produced alongside David Brown's own agricultural tractor the VAK1. As peace returned the flood gates opened and by 1948 the firm were making and selling 100 tractors a week. As the years progressed, David Brown's grew into a corporation, and new gear plants were acquired or opened at Sunderland, Salford, Solihull and North London. By the time I joined the company, the application of the gearing division's products were found in the aircraft, automotive and railway industries, steel mills, pulp mills, paper mills, sugar mills, armoured fighting vehicles and ship building to

Tom Lazenby shows a new DB 25 tractor to Prince Philip, David Brown and Lionel Harper, MD of Massey - Harris UK

name but a few. They also owned the famous luxury and sporting car manufacturers Aston-Martin Lagonda, and the ship-building firms of John L. Thornycroft Ltd and Vospers Ltd. Other divisions of the company produced pumps, industrial heating equipment, honing equipment, microwave ovens, interior design and furnishing contracts and industrial oil burning equipment. It was an empire presided over by David (now a knight of the realm), and an army of able Lieutenant Generals which included his son, also called David Brown (and often referred to as David Brown junior).

Smithfield Show 1950

The firm's tractor group was a major operation in its own right and it had ten subsidiary companies. The principal one was Harrison, McGregor & Guest Ltd. at the Albion Works, Leigh, Lancashire. Overseas companies were found in New South Wales, Australia; Belfast, Ireland; East London, South Africa; Dublin, Eire; Pennsylvania, USA; Hanover, West Germany; and Roskilde, Denmark. The company was then the largest British-owned producer of agricultural tractors, with 80% of the output going for export. The dealer network numbered some 2,508 agents in 100 lands. It was an organisation which one could be proud to be a part of, and it was still run as a small family firm until it 'merged' with J.I. Case, part of the huge Tenneco Group from the United States in 1972. The end of David Brown control is a topic which we will discuss in a future volume, but for now I hand over to Leonard Craven, who began his days in the tractor industry with Harry Ferguson and David Brown back in 1936.

Chapter 1
In At The Start

'I find it hard to believe that it is now more than sixty years since I was given the unique opportunity to take an active part in constructing the first small batch of what was then, the revolutionary farm tractor invented by Harry Ferguson, and built and marketed in conjunction with the David Brown organisation. It subsequently proved to be a revolution in the world of agriculture as the demand for farm mechanisation developed. It was in the spring of 1936 that I made my way into one of the massive machine shops of the Park Works factory. David Browns were acknowledged to be "the World's Finest Gear Makers", and there were literally hundreds of metal-working machines operating in this immense one-storey building. One corner had been cleared however and an area of about twenty yards square was now occupied by half a dozen fitters' benches and an untidy stack of material. From this pile of parts a small band of four or five fitters were endeavouring to put together the very first batch of Ferguson Brown tractors to come off the production line. There were also five Coventry Climax "E" type engines (which were fitted as standard to the first 350 tractors). Three of these had been fitted with a bell-housing and clutch mechanism and were in the process of being mated up with transmission and rear axle units which had been constructed on adjacent benches. The foreman, Harry Pilkington, and his fitters were experiencing some difficulty in finding the necessary parts from the untidy heap of material that had been dumped on the shop floor. It was my duty to identify the components, match them up to the delivery notes and locate them in the metal bins that had been temporarily erected on the site. The first building sanction was for 100 tractors, and material ordered from outside suppliers was already arriving in an ever increasing stream. By the time that the first 5 tractors were ready, it was evident that more space was needed. Therefore the operation was transferred to the upper three floors of what had been the Automobile Gearbox plant. The first floor was the tractor assembly area, the second eventually housed the engine assembly, implements were built on the third and the fourth was given over to painting and "finishing". Additional labour was recruited, mostly from the ranks of the workforce of the Karrier Motors who had recently closed down their Huddersfield factory.

Testing the DB prototype engine

I remember the names of Fred Armitage, Harry Brown, John Cook, Harold Idle, Bill Wallace, Bernard North, Harry Dobson, Jeff Lee, Ernest Kenyon, Jimmy Milnes, Jim Kenny, Godwin Atkinson and Bill Dearnley in the assembly team, backed up by Sam Crosland and Harry Hall as general labourers - not forgetting the apprentices, Norman Calvert, Leslie Nunns, Norman Whitley and Trevor Noble; Harold Hawkes and Harry Lockley were the painters and the quality control inspector was Emil Moes, an expatriate Belgian who now fluently spoke the broad Yorkshire dialect. The manager was Harold Thompson who had been recruited from the Midlands. However, the man with the most difficult job was Mr. Cosgrave, who was responsible for organising a steady flow of the right material, at the right time to the tractor assembly line. The completed tractors were transferred to Harry Ferguson's premises which were located in the former Karrier Works in nearby Cable Street from where the marketing and distribution processes were controlled. Quite frequently, Harry Ferguson accompanied by John Chambers together with his henchmen, Greer and Sands visited the assembly line, - where they became known as "the Cable Street Gang". Although their visits were usually in connection with some technical problem, they did tend to interfere somewhat with the normal operations. Consequently, over the months, their welcome became less cordial. Harry Ferguson was undoubtedly a genius, but he had his eccentricities which were difficult to understand, and quite often absolutely unacceptable to more ordinary people. One can give some credence to his fetish 'that under no consideration must the weight of his tractor exceed that of a plough horse' - after all, there was the problem of soil compression! The majority of the nuts and bolts on the Ferguson-Brown products had either $7/16$" or $5/8$" BSF thread, but the maestro was not satisfied with the reliability of ordinary standard steel bolts. He insisted on using only special 'Hitensile' bolts, and all the nuts had to be case-hardened in the Heat Treatment department. Such was his obsession with ensuring the reliability of bolted components, that he could frequently be seen, particularly in the implement assembly shop, literally hanging (with his feet off the ground) onto a specially made five foot extension welded on to an engineer's spanner - making sure that the nut was securely tightened! Many of the highly experienced fitters on the workforce protested that this was contrary to the ethics of good engineering. Some even refusing point blank to use anything but the standard spanner, creating quite a tricky situation for the personnel department. One is tempted to wonder if there could be some link with the fact that the Ferguson operation over the years moved from David Browns to Ford, then to Standard and finally from Standard to Massey Harris?

DB staff with the first Ferguson Brown

By the end of the year the first hundred tractors had been built and the Ferguson organisation had succeeded in creating a growing demand for the product in a market which had a traditional reputation of resistance to innovation. A further sanction for 250 tractors and sets of implements ensured continuity of the operation. The new engine assembly department was installed on the second floor, and by the time the 350th tractor rolled off the line, the David Brown engine was available to be fitted as standard to the next sanction for five hundred tractors. The new power unit was based on the previous Coventry Climax design, suitable for petrol/TVO fuel. The cylinder bore was $3^{1}/_{8}"$ as opposed to $3^{1}/_{4}"$; the oil sump was larger and an oil-bath air filter fitted as standard to combat dusty working conditions. The marketing team were really getting their message across, and the demand for this innovative tractor continued to increase by leaps and bounds. Local authorities discovered that this lively and highly manoeuvrable machine was eminently suitable for a variety of urban applications in parks, gardens and cemeteries. When fitted with a rotary brush it was also ideal for street cleansing operations. There was even an order for four Ferguson Brown tractors to be delivered to a customer in South Africa to operate underground in diamond mines. A number of tractors had been exported to the Scandinavian countries to be used in forestry work, but the strain imposed on the aluminium gear box casing resulted in a large proportion of the vehicles literally "breaking their backs". The David Brown engineers prescribed the use of a steel or cast-iron gear box casing, but the Ferguson lobby were adamant in their rejection of this, as this would increase the weight of the machine beyond the limits specified by its inventor. Eventually a compromise was agreed; the material specification for the gear box was changed to RR50 - a very expensive light alloy! Purely as a matter of interest, the part number of the modified component was G110. Many of the customers for the Ferguson Brown tractor were 'first time' buyers, and they were taking the first step to mechanisation by acquiring a tractor to take over some of the work formerly done by horses. There were some amusing anecdotes brought back to the factory by the field service operators ... like the farmer who always shouted "Gee up!" when starting to move, and "Whoa!" when stopping or applying the brakes ... and one who, when reporting a radiator leak, said "She be awful thirsty of late".

The name was by now firmly established in the United Kingdom, and an ever increasing flow of orders resulted in a further extension of the building sanction for another five hundred units. In the early part of 1938 the production target of 10 tractors per week was finally achieved. Significantly, although no further building sanction for the Ferguson Brown tractor was issued, the David Brown organisation purchased the extensive Meltham Mills factory site with the declared intention of using it as a tractor manufacturing plant. There had been a small but persistent demand for a stronger and more durable gear box housing in spite of the concessionary RR50 component approved by the Ferguson team. In response to external pressures the David Brown engineers in conjunction with the David Brown Foundry at Penistone produced about a dozen 'meehanite' cast-iron gearbox cases to be supplied to selected customers. This was of course without the sanction - and hopefully without the knowledge of Ferguson - such was the widening rift between the two partners. Thirteen hundred and fifty Ferguson Brown's were produced over the period of three years. The last 14 being completed at Meltham Mills some months after the new David Brown Tractor had made its triumphal debut at the 1939 Royal Agricultural Societies show at Windsor.' Ferguson was busying himself in America, meanwhile, having 'meaningful discussions' with Henry Ford. It can be rightly said that the Ferguson Brown tractor revolutionised the British agricultural equipment manufacturing industry, and it was the first stage in two great Marques. As Tom Lazenby remembers: 'David Brown saw in his partnership with Harry Ferguson the long-sought opportunity to build and market a complete end-product under the David Brown name. There was no doubt that this vision went far beyond the 1,336 tractors that would eventually be made at the Lockwood factory. According to Harry Ferguson the tractor was to be called the Ferguson, but when it was launched to the press by the DB Publicity Department its name had been changed to the Ferguson Brown; and this was but the first of many disagreements.' As time progressed the differences grew and, as Herbert Ashfield recalls, 'when the Ferguson Brown tractors were not selling particularly well, David Brown began to enquire why! It was therefore shown to him that the model needed a number of modifications to make it acceptable to the majority of British farmers. However, when he pressed Ferguson to make these improvements, his partner would not alter his design one little bit.' With this, the rift turned into an unbridgeable chasm, and David Brown decided to break the partnership and produce his own tractor. Yet, until such time as that could be produced, the Ferguson Brown continued in production. Whereas the official records account for one thousand three hundred and fifty Ferguson Brown tractors being produced we can now reveal that, in actual fact, 1,351 were made and sold!   On this point it is fitting to let Leonard Craven conclude the account; 'In the early part of 1940, a very special friend of 'the Boss' expressed a desire for one of these now 'out of production' machines, and as a very special favour it was decided to make one from the Replacement Parts Department stock. I know that this happened because I was the storekeeper who issued the parts to the Service workshop for assembly.' Tractor No. 1, pictured inset, is now preserved at the Massey - Ferguson Heritage Centre, Banner Lane, Coventry.

Chapter 2
VAK 1 1939-1945

As the problems with Ferguson became insoluble, David Brown's design team began the first tentative steps toward the production of their own, independent tractor. However, as work on the Ferguson-Brown was still continuing at Park Works, the project had to be carried out without any publicity. Prior to commencing this project, David Brown had met Alex Taub of General Motors who provided invaluable advice and encouragement. This had finally convinced Brown that his new engine should be made to a completely new design, and use overhead valves and wet sleeves. Accordingly, David Brown engaged a designer by the name of Albert Kersey who he secreted away in an isolated drawing office at Park Works. To maintain the secrecy, the design team referred to their new project by a clandestine code name, VAK1, which meant Vehicle Agricultural Kerosene One. Leonard Craven remembers the time well, writing 'During 1938 it became evident that all was not well at the top. Visits by Ferguson and 'the Cable Street gang' became more sporadic, and

Wooden mock-up of the VAK at Park Works c.1938

the former spirit of camaraderie and comradeship was noticeably at a premium. What was more significant however was the 'cloak and dagger' activity on the top floor, which was virtually designated a "No Go" area to all but the team of David Brown engineers who were examining in great detail tractors made by other manufacturers. I remember seeing Ford, John Deere, Allis Chalmers and Massey Harris machines on various occasions. This culminated in the erection of a full sized "dummy" model of a machine which eventually emerged as the new David Brown Tractor.' The new David Brown engine was completed on 13th December 1938, and it ran on its test-bed with considerable ease - which was obviously a great relief to all concerned! The next stage was the completion of the prototype David Brown tractor, so the small 'research and development' team worked on in secret - often working long into the dark winter evenings. As the work on the machine neared completion one evening in January, David Brown told his men to knock off at midnight and finish it off the next day. However, after he had gone they all decided to carry on until the tractor was done. They worked until

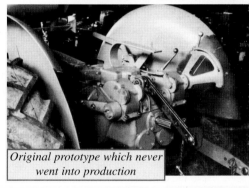

Original prototype which never went into production

the small hours to complete the final adjustments and then, on finishing the tractor, Ernest Kenyon got the bright idea to drive it up to David Brown's house, Durker Roods at Meltham, so that the 'boss' could see his new machine. It is reputed that the great man was awakened around 3am by the revving engine and a group of grinning, cheering men. Brown then came down to see his first completed machine in dressing gown pyjamas and slippers, and then they all toasted the success of the David Brown Tractor with his best malt whisky. More work was to be done on the tractor, and several modifications were indicated after its initial field tests. These tests were quite extreme and, as Leonard Craven recalls, 'It was decided to test the tractor to destruction, to see which components gave up first. In its grey paint it was taken out on a circuit around Meltham which took it up Wessendenhead Road to the Isle of Skye Hotel; from there it followed the Saddleworth - Holmfirth road back to the Ford Inn from where it returned to Meltham.' It was a demanding route which reached an altitude of 1,506 feet [460 metres] above sea level, and on one or two occasions it was actually buried deep into snow-drifts and had to be recovered. In view of the secrecy it was run on this route mostly at night time, an unenviable task

Prototype VAK on test

shared by Bill Harrison and a small team of other drivers who braved the winter weather on the Pennine moors. The tractor was, however, to be kept running for 24 hours a day and some of the testing was carried out on David Brown's own land or in the quarries at Royd Edge. Then, in even more secrecy, the tractor was taken to a farm at Middleton Tyas in North Yorkshire where it was put under further stress and strain. Fortunately, these tests and the subsequent improvements were concluded just in time for a re-styled VAK1 to be prepared for the 1939 Royal Agricultural Show which was held at Windsor Great Park that July. The biggest difficulty to be faced by the team was actually what colour to paint their new tractor, and the obvious choice of brown was widely discussed and almost equally rejected. When the decision over the colour scheme became heated, it is said that David Brown sent for his red hunting jacket,

Production VAK in use as fire engine c.1942

and then threw this on to the tractor and said 'paint it that colour'. A task which was duly completed by Harold Hawkes and Harry Lockley the company's two tractor painters. Thus was born the unusual and distinctive livery which, quite appropriately, was known to all and sundry as 'hunting pink'. The models that were to be sent to the show were given much extra detail, and all the external bolt heads that were visible were fitted with bright chromium-plated bolts. The same bright finish was applied to the headlamps and to other small parts, though these would have normally been painted red or black. This set a trend for many of the show tractors which followed over the years. Bright, stylish and attractive they may have been, but to the down-to-earth Yorkshiremen who built them, they were known inside the works as the 'pansy tractors'.

The 1939 Windsor Show model

With its 3.5" bore petrol or TVO engine and 4-speed gear box, some 5,350 VAK1s were to be produced between 1939 and 1945, including some Utility versions. As Bert Ashfield recalls 'When we were making the Ferguson Brown we had the advantage of Ferguson patents but after the split we had to get round these; they were mainly concerned with getting weight transfer from the plough to the tractor's rear wheels, and also with getting the plough to follow. We got over the depth control problem by putting an adjustable land wheel on the implement which completely overcame that part of the patent. The convergent linkage problem was solved by someone coming up with the brilliant idea of parallel linkage and a z-cross shaft. This meant that instead of the inclination being on the links, it was put on the cross shaft, so when the plough moved off centre the z-shaft fetched it back. That was our way of getting around the Ferguson patents, but virtually every other traction manufacturer, including Ford (after a spectacular law suit), paid him a royalty on his convergent linkage patents. Another matter was the original bolt-on power lift which used the Ferguson pump and a number of Ferguson parts. We decided to put our own control valve on the VAK1, to get round the patent, but this wasn't really satisfactory. We eventually got the power lift right on the VAK1, but this wasn't until about the time when we went on to the Cropmaster. So, although we had our trials with the power lift, we did avoid the Ferguson patents; for example, one of these showed that their control valve was on the suction side, so we put our control valve on the delivery side and got over that.'

The VAK made its way to its first public appearance by rail, being sent by the LMS from Meltham station, which was later destined to become the starting point for thousands of tractors which would be despatched by rail. The tractors that were sent were all sheeted over, as great efforts were made to conceal their actual appearance until their arrival at the show

VAK1's roll off the Meltham Mills production line in 1942

imposed) and, as Albert Kersey told my father, 'after that it was sink or swim'. However, David was not idle in this period and he succeeded in getting more work from the various Government ministries. It was, unfortunately, this work which nearly made the dream of a David Brown Tractor stillborn. At the time the war began in September 1939, such tractor production as there was, was still being carried out at Park Works, for the Meltham Mills factory did not exist as such, save as a collection of large abandoned buildings full of redundant textile machinery. After a massive clearing up operation, work began in fitting out the factory for engineering purposes, but the Ministry of Supply were already becoming increasingly reluctant to allow supplies of steel for the manufacture of tractors. In one conversation, a regional supply officer told David Brown 'why do farmers need tractors, they've used horses for centuries'. Another factor in this attitude against tractor manufacture in Britain was the fact that American tractors were available to Britain via the Lease-Lend scheme, whereas military equipment was not. Bert Ashfield confirms officialdoms approach, saying 'When I started, the VAK1 was on ration as they were only allowed to make so many agricultural tractors a week. They had contracts for Air Ministry tractors, the VIG1, for which there was an insatiable demand. It didn't matter how many they made, because more were always needed. However, on the back of this production they allowed us to make a set number of agricultural tractors. This was primarily because we used mounted implements behind the VAK1, and these only used about a third of the steel that a conventional implement needed. There was a big demand for ploughs because, due to the massive increase in food production, a lot of pre-war ploughs were rapidly wearing out. As the Government were having to allocate materials to replace them, they decided to send the steel to us as we could produce a plough for the VAK1 for about a third of the cost of a conventional trailed implement. The VAK1 prospered because of this and

ground. However, after the wagons arrived at the GWR station yard in Windsor, it was found that the paint-work on the bonnets had been badly rubbed by the heavy tarpaulin sheets which were used on the railways. Very hasty arrangements had to be made for coach painters to be hired locally so that the problem could be resolved in time for pristine tractors to be shown on the stand. The stand of David Brown Tractors Ltd. Huddersfield carried both Ferguson advertising banners and Ferguson-Brown tractors, but the main focus for attention was undoubtedly the VAK1. In its hunting pink livery and with a cockpit arrangement for the driver, it was a truly resplendent and stylish tractor. It was also in stark contrast to most of the other tractors then being displayed, and as a consequence it was an immediate success with both the farming press and those who would actually use it. It is reported that orders for over 3,000 tractors were taken, though Harry Ferguson's reaction on seeing the VAK1, is said to be entirely unprintable.

The outbreak of war in September 1939 coincided with the formal break up of the Brown - Ferguson partnership. Ferguson would have nothing to do with David Brown's new model, so Brown bought out Ferguson's shares (and those of his friends), paying them pound for pound on their investment. The threat of war considerably strengthened David Brown's position, as he believed that hostilities would create a massive demand for all types of tractor. With a lease for the mills secured on favourable terms, orders at hand for the VAK1, and a good design and engineering team established, the tractor operation moved to the 400,000 square feet of the Meltham Mills factory. It is believed that Frank Brown told his son that he would offer a limited amount of support (possibly with a twelve month term being

we made a total of 5,000 in the period of 1940-44. That's around 1,000 a year - not bad going for the war years.' Indeed it was not bad going at all, but already a successor for the VAK1 was becoming essential if David Brown were to build on this success and the last build order for this model was sanctioned in October 1944!

VAK demonstrator at work in 1943

Chapter 3
VTK1 and VIG1
1941 - 1949

With the work that David Brown Gears were doing on tank transmissions in the 1930s, and the firm's development into agricultural products, it is not surprising that the company would apply this technology to military use in the form of a tracked tractor. Actually, David Brown wanted to start producing a tracked tractor shortly after his split with Harry Ferguson, but he was initially prohibited from doing so because of the difficulties with his father over space at Lockwood, the subsequent move to Meltham Mills and the outbreak of war. He held this goal constantly in mind in the late 1930s, because he had a strong feeling that the country would soon be crying out for tracked vehicles as well as agricultural tractors. When the Ministry of Supply assessed the output potential of Meltham Mills, it was patently obvious that the two areas of war production where David Brown could provide both experience and capacity, would be the manufacture of tank gear boxes and aero gears/components. Indeed throughout the period 1940-45, Meltham Mills turned out 10,000 tank transmissions, 125,000 aero gears, and 6,000 hydraulic pumps for aircraft. However, Lord Beaverbrook (Minister for Aircraft Production) put a forceful argument to Winston Churchill that the tractors he needed for towing medium to heavy bombers, could not be acquired by lease-lend under the terms of the Stockholm Convention which outlined the issues of neutrality. As the aerodrome construction programme was then considered to be of the utmost national importance, a decision was taken to order a tracked vehicle which could then be later used for towing duties. With the experience gained in tank transmissions, the time was indeed ripe for Brown's to commence production of a tracked vehicle for the Air Ministry. The story of the RAF track-layer (pictured centre right) is quite fascinating, as it was designed to fulfil the Ministry's concept of a dual-purpose tractor with a powerful winch, which could be used either in aerodrome construction or in aircraft towing. Yet both of these roles were, in many ways, completely incompatible with one another. As J. C. R. Birney then Sales Manager of David Browns wrote in *Tractor News* at the end of the war, 'the machine was a bastard - in more ways than one'. The design had been rapidly evolved in conjunction with experts from the RAF, and it resulted in what was little more than a tracked version of the VAK1. Whilst the tractor performed its tests reasonably well, in service the machine was far from ideal.

As Herbert Ashfield remembers 'The original aircraft tracklayer the VTK1 may have been a good idea on paper, but unfortunately it was so slow that it wasn't really a practical proposition on a busy aerodrome. It had been conceived by people who's idea of an airfield was literally a field, and a tracklayer was not really what was needed at all. Our model had a top speed of five miles an hour, but at anything over this it would shake itself to bits. Sometimes it had to tow an aircraft over a mile, and it took too much time to do this.'

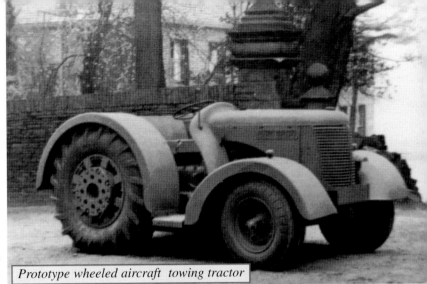

Prototype wheeled aircraft towing tractor

VTK 1

Bomb loading operations

Indeed, in many other ways it was proving itself to be quite unsuitable for the RAF's purpose, because when they began using crawlers for aircraft towing or bombing up procedures, they found that the metal crawler tracks were not doing a lot of good to the runways and aprons. The Ministry soon decided that it wasn't a crawler that was wanted at all, but a wheeled tractor - could David Brown's oblige? They certainly could, and a hasty re-design and conversion programme was set in motion.

All the tracked machines were recalled to Meltham and along with wheeled machines these were then supplied as wheeled tractors. As these were returned to the works, large numbers of them began building up in the goods yard at Meltham station and they were soon found to be clogging up the space needed for tank transmissions that were being brought in for gearbox work, not to mention the tractors which the company were despatching to supply depots around the country. They then began to build up a dump of VTK1s at Lockwood station, then Honley and finally at Penistone. Many of these were then moved to the firm's Penistone works until the time could be found to convert them. As the picture top right shows, considerable thought was put into how these tractors might be profitably re-worked for other applications.

Herbert Ashfield remembers the decision was taken to convert the tractors for both industrial and agricultural use; 'Nearly all the VTK1s were sent back and converted to wheeled tractors, so that alongside the VAK1 and VAK1A we were offering an industrial tractor, which we were able to achieve by modifying Air Ministry tracklayers and tractors for civilian use. After the war was over, we got a lot back and converted them for peaceful use, turning them into threshing tractors.' It can also be revealed that some of the salesmen were often known to quote a little bit of the Bible when selling these tractors, as they said they were figuratively fulfilling the scripture in Isaiah Chapter 2 verse 4 which says 'they shall pound their swords into hoes and their spears into pruning hooks' (Bible In Living English).

In all some 185 VTK1s were produced, and a large number of these were re-worked into conventional wheeled tractors. When the combined production of the Air Ministry and VIG1/100 tractors are taken into consideration, the total production run was 2,400 which, surprisingly compares favourably to almost half the production figure on the VAK1 and two-thirds the total production of the VAK1A, yet these sturdy, handsome looking tractors are often largely ignored in accounts of the company's early days. Based on VAK1 and 1A tractors, these heavy industrial models had the same 37 BHP petrol engine but were fitted with a low-speed final drive for towing. Some were fitted with conventional clutches, but others were provided with fluid drive torque converters. At least four of these tractors were developed as shunting tractors and one, known colloquially as 'Muffin The Mule', spent years shunting the internal railway system at the company's Penistone Works.

VTK Tracklayer at Meltham

'Thresherman' conversion

Heavy industrial tractor

Chapter 4
VAK 1A 1945 - 1947

In 1943 G. S. Reekie set out David Brown's development position saying 'Our agricultural and industrial machines will be just as vital after the War as in the present circumstances and the plant and equipment is therefore poised for quick expansion, as soon as more stable conditions permit the divergence of materials to the constructive purposes of peace. Given the freedom of action we should be in a position to make a very large contribution towards the large number of tractors that the Ministry of Agriculture estimate to be the annual post-war requirements for the British Isles'. While the main efforts of the company were concentrated on the VAK1 and military requirements throughout the war, design work went on and an improved agricultural tractor, the VAK2, was conceived for peace-time conditions. The four main improvements envisaged for this model were a) a combined inlet and exhaust manifold to give better idling on kerosene; b) a gearbox with six forward and two reverse speeds; c) a hydraulic system which was in-built instead of optional; d) more robust final drives. Yet this model never came to fruition, as sales in post-war

VAK1 utility version 1943

A VAK1 and VAK1A at work in the heavy clays of Lincolnshire c.1947

Britain were very buoyant and all the production capacity was needed to fulfil orders for VAK1s. Indeed, a continuing restriction in the supplies of various raw materials, coupled with the national austerity period, necessitated the continuing production of this model, and the company found it very hard to institute the much needed changes that it both wanted and had to make. However, with the decision taken not to produce the VAK2, the company opted to progressively introduce the improvements it had decided to embody within this tractor into a modified version of the VAK1. Thus was born the VAK1A, which appeared in the early spring of 1945. In this model the improved inlet and manifold was incorporated, although the other three features were not to appear for a further three years when the VAK1C was introduced. Tom Lazenby was involved in these early days of post-war development, having started with the company

just before the VAK1 ended its production run. 'They were on VAK1s when I started and very soon afterwards we brought in the VAK1A, which was the first tractor that we had built which had got all the bugs out of it. We would have got rid of what should have been teething problems in the new design years earlier, but the war virtually stopped our agricultural tractor production and we had no chance to bring in improvements. After the war the demand was for more and more tractors, and in these the farmers were wanting increased horse power and diesel engines. The war had really changed things; farming, manufacturing, people's perceptions (including ourselves), and above all our ideas at David Brown's. So, as we became accustomed to peace-time conditions, we gradually began to improve as we went along. Most times we were overcoming problems that had arisen between 1939 and 1945; sometimes these were production problems, or service problems and sometimes even sales problems, all of which were holding back the tractors at various times. Now around this time we had a market research programme undertaken, which had told us

Prototype VAK1A

Early VAK1A in Meltham Mills village

time Ford tractors were having a great deal of trouble with paraffin running down the cylinder walls causing a lot of wear, but with the new manifold we didn't get any of these problems. We also redesigned the transmission, and the power lift and we were well satisfied that the VAK1A would carry us through the next couple of years until things became a bit more settled. Unfortunately, the 1B, which was the tractor with a new gear box, didn't go ahead as sales of the 1A did very well indeed and production of this model ran a lot longer than we ever thought it would.' As with the VAK1, the 3.5" bore engine was petrol or TVO, and it had a 4-speed gear box and all-speed governors, though an optional 6-speed gearbox was introduced in 1948. From 1949 onwards, when David Browns began making a diesel engine option for the VAK1C, farmers could add a new dimension to their VAK1s with the purchase of a manifold conversion kit. The Sales Manager JCR Birney, later wrote 'In view of the large numbers of the earlier David Brown models that were still in service, the firm offered a conversion kit for all its TVO engines. This was available at about one third of the price of a new engine, it prolonged the life of many of those tractors and it bred a new era of brand loyalty to the David Brown Marque.' Altogether 5,350 VAK1As were produced at Meltham Mills, with a final batch being sanctioned at the end of January which ran to some 352 in total. The last VAK1A (No.9852) rolled down the assembly line in June 1947, in the midst of a string of VAK1Cs which had come into production two months earlier. The VAK1A had been an admirable stop gap, but it was the advent of its successor which would really set David Brown's name and product range in the list of all-time great tractor manufacturers.

that the market for tractors was at least a hundred thousand a year in Great Britain. Nobody in Britain had the capacity for that production, so a great deal of the tractors would have to be imported, though David Brown reckoned we could easily make and sell one hundred tractors a week. I would have thought that we were the only people in the tractor business that knew what the demand was likely to be, and we set our stall out to capture the potential business that we had calculated from the rate at which it was judged that farmers would change from horses to tractors.' It was abundantly clear, that in this time of change the VAK, hastily introduced and still suffering from basic shortcomings in the original design, would have to be modified if David Brown's were going to break into the tractor market in a big way.

Herbert Ashfield recalls how the development came about; 'By the end of the war the days of the VAK1 were coming to an end, as it was only natural they should, because it had been made in a fair hurry in 1939 and its short-comings were well known by 1944. After the VAK2 tractor was dropped, we decided to modify the VAK1 and the idea was to produce further models known as the 1A, 1B, 1C and 1D. The main problems with the VAK1 were associated with the manifold and the fact that you had to run it quite a while on petrol, before switching over to paraffin; even then, when it idled, it used to pop and back-fire. It was quite a problem so one of the first things we did was to put in a new manifold and diverted the exhaust round the intake, so that the exhaust warmed the intake air. With this, once it had warmed up it would idle without any trouble. At the same

Early production model VAK1A

Chapter Number 5
VAK1C Cropmaster
1947 - 1954

One of the most famous models in the David Brown stable was the VAK1C, or the Cropmaster as it was better known. In total some 59,800 models were manufactured, making this series of tractor numerically second only to the 990 models. The VAK1C was introduced in April 1947 in time for the round of summer agricultural shows, but David Brown said that he wanted his new tractor to be the star at its first show. Accordingly, the Sales Department came up with a bright idea for its launch, and they decided to have their own show exclusively featuring the equipment made by David Brown and those companies with whom they were associated. This was held on land just off the Harrogate - Pateley Bridge road, and it became known as the Harrogate Convention. When the Cropmaster was presented to the farming public at this event that April, it was billed as the tractor which embodied all the four major improvements that Brown's had intended to put into the VAK2. As we have seen David Brown's had intended that a VAK1B would be built to incorporate a 6-speed gearbox, but it was never introduced and this facility only became available as an optional extra on the VAK1A . Yet the success of these 6-speed VAK1As encouraged the Sales Department, and in turn this prompted the firm to move on to the VAK1C. This development firmly pushed the proposed VAK2 into the realms of a 'might have been', and the decision to carry on the VAK1 designation was taken because the 1C embodied so many features of its two forerunners. It is also worth mentioning the decision to introduce the name Cropmaster other than the simple alpha-numerical designation that had been hitherto employed. This came about as a consequence of the development of David Brown's marketing department, who brought their influence to bear on how the company's models were presented. At this time they hit on the 'master' concept, and designations such as Cropmaster, Taskmaster and

VAK1C Prototype at Meltham Mills Football Ground with Cropmaster name

VAK1C Prototype at Meltham Mills Football Ground with David Brown name painted in large letters

Cropmaster Diesel prototype

original Ferguson was that a farmer had to buy a tractor plus a set of implements. They didn't like it because they wanted to use their own ploughs and trailed implements, but Ferguson wouldn't make any provision for using their old equipment. So if a farmer didn't buy a set of implements the tractor was virtually useless! It was one of the points that David Brown fell out with him on, and he said to his design team "Well, why can't we have a draw-bar and then the farmers could hitch their old trailed ploughs up." So on the VAK1 they made provision for the trailed implements, but you've got to remember that there were no mounted implements in those days. So if you sold a tractor suited for mounted implements, you've got to sell mounted implements. Well, we couldn't make enough mounted implements to meet the demand, so our tractor was made with a button-on power lift. Because of this we could sell the tractor with or without a power lift on it, as it still had a draw-bar suitable for trailed implements. When we got the 1C we made an in-built power lift so it was suitable for trailed implements or mounted implements. In a way the 1C was the big brother to the 1A, and because it was so versatile we sold so many. But it was the chance to change from a petrol/TVO engine which made such a big difference."

Trackmaster were born. Around the same time, David Brown decided that his name should also appear in large letters on the tractor, as he felt that the world should know that he was the originator of the red tractors. Some may consider this conceited, but he was only exploiting his name and reputation in the same way the Ferguson and Ford were exploiting their's.

The range of implements available with the Cropmaster also grew, and in this the VAK1C became a popular British farm tractor and it greatly speeded up post-war farming mechanisation. Herbert Ashfield writes 'The 3.5" Bore 35.0 BHP VAK1C included our own power lift which we made in built. This was done because one of the problems with selling the

The VAK1C became available as a 31.5 BHP diesel-engined variety in 1949, with the first units being tested in the spring prior to an autumn launch just ahead of the Smithfield Show. It was a unique first for David Browns, and they became the first major tractor manufacturer in Britain to launch their own make diesel engine. Yet, this had long been a goal of the company, and when designing the VAK1 engine David

Vineyard Cropmaster

Brown and Albert Kersey had shown the engine plans to Harry Ricardo, who was one of the leading consultants on diesel engines in the 1930s. Brown asked Ricardo what modifications would be required to the design if the engine were ever Diesellised, to which he was advised to strengthen the camshafts and connecting rods. The tooling for the VAK1 engine included these modifications, and this saved much time and money when the market for introducing a diesel engine finally developed. Tom Lazenby recalls the introduction of the Cropmaster Diesel with some pride 'The Cropmaster was a grand little tractor, but the Cropmaster Diesel when it came in was magnificent and the salesmen could sell that like hot cakes. I

Super Cropmaster tricycle tractor 1950

Cropmaster with front mounted splitter

remember when we launched the diesel at Smithfield Show, Ford's Sales Manager at the time, Frankie Daniels, came up to me and said "I wish we had that." So I took him to have a closer look at it, and when we turned the engine over he said "it's marvellous, it runs just like a sewing machine - that's what we want, not an old slab-sided design like ours. Imagine, if you took a good engine like that and put it in the Fordson Major." So we went over and looked at his tractor, and with barely concealed envy he said "Its twenty-five years out of date this and it needs a thumping bag of tricks in here to improve it. I've seen your engine before of course, and I told the boss (at Ford) if you want to see what's wrong with our engines, go up to Yorkshire and have a look at a real tractor, the Cropmaster diesel." I don't think we could have got any higher praise than that!'

The Cropmaster sold very well, and in the years between 1947 and 1953 the firm made a number of variants. One of the first was the Cropmaster M, a model without hydraulic lift, which was available from April 1947 in the standard engine and as a diesel variant from June 1950. Next came the Vineyard, or narrow, version, which had a particular application with a lot of overseas customers as well as market gardeners in this country. A few of these Vineyard models could also be ordered with dealer modifications which made them into a low-clearance tractor, and a lot of these sold well in the West Country and other locations where farms had small entrances in the barns, byres and storehouses etc. Quite a few of these 'specials' were sold to the fruit growers, among which cider-apple farmers were the most common. A diesel engine version was introduced to the Vineyard tractor in 1951, but the demand for these was so low that only a small number (around 80) were produced. In time for the 1950 Smithfield Show the company introduced the Super Cropmaster, with a 3⅝" bore TVO engine which delivered a power range of 35-37.5 brake horse power. The tractor featured large section tyres, and tin-work which had distinctive full-engine side panels with grill vents. One of the tin-work fitters, Albert Haigh, recalls them as being called 'the fishy tractors' in the factory because the

vents looked more like the gills on a big shark'. A novel introduction brought about from a demand in the Canadian market, saw the inclusion of a rain-trap in the exhaust/silencer unit.

In all, approaching 5,000 Super Cropmasters were built before they were discontinued at the end of 1952. As there was a demand for low-clearance and narrow tractors, there was also an emerging demand for tractors with a high clearance, and as a consequence of this demand the Prairie version of the Cropmaster emerged in October 1951. Tom Lazenby recalls the introduction of this variant; 'When we brought in the Prairie tractor it was aimed at the Canadian and United States market, and we had to make it look a bit different. So we got round a few ideas and tarted up the tractor; you know, different wings, wide mudguards and single seats, which we hoped would kid the Americans that we'd got something really special for them.' The Prairie model did have a very striking appearance, a fact which was much remarked on when it appeared (once again) in time for the Smithfield Show that December. A 34.5 BHP diesel version was brought out the following autumn, and unlike the Vineyard diesel these sold reasonably well. In fact the Cropmaster Prairie Diesel actually accounted for about a third of the total production figures of this dependable variant.

Other versions of the Cropmaster appeared in industrial form as the Taskmaster and as a tracked version called the Trackmaster, both of which feature elsewhere in this book. In all 59,800 Cropmasters were produced before they were superseded by stripped down versions which appeared in 1953 in response to competition brought about by the mass production of Ford and Ferguson tractors.

Super Cropmaster with Rasspe Mower at Meltham Hall in 1950

Chapter 6
Tracklayers
1942 - 1963

As we have seen earlier, the first endeavour of David Brown into the crawler market was hardly what could have been called a roaring success as the VTK1 Air Ministry Tracklayer was really an abysmal failure. But David Browns had already invested a not insubstantial amount of time and money into the crawler production. Fortunately, one of the RAF track-layers had been loaned some months earlier to the Royal Engineers for work on sea defences in East Anglia. They were delighted with what they had seen, as it showed that at least one British manufacturer had the potential to make a crawler tractor and this would help them get round the strict embargo on buying equipment for military purposes from what were still neutral countries at the time. True, American-made crawlers were being purchased, but technically it was illegal to use these for any sort of offensive or defensive works.

Wooden mock-up for the Trackmaster 1947

Thus, in 1942, was born the David Brown DB4 a 38.5 hp crawler which was fitted with a Dorman Ricardo diesel engine and a 5-speed box. These were first successfully employed in the North African campaign, where the DB4 could traverse ground in which a wheeled machine would become bogged down. Fifty or so DB4 crawlers were used at Normandy immediately after the Allied beach-head was established there in June 1944, and their success in this exercise led to the Government requisitioning three more large batches in 1944, and five batches in 1945. We are not quite sure how many DB4 s were made altogether, but a figure of 110 is shown in some records as being the total number made before production ended on Wednesday 12th January 1949.

Prototype Trackmaster on Meltham Moor 1948

DB4 Tracklayer with Dorman engine

Undoubtedly, the DB4 track-layer was seen as being useful for civilian purposes too. The rigours of war had shown it could take any amount of abuse, and compared itself well against many of the American dozers, scrapers and crawlers that were flowing into Britain or which were sold as war surplus by the Americans after 1945. These ex-WD DB4s subsequently found employment in airfield work, forestry, road-making, and all-manner of reconstruction work projects in France, Holland and Belgium. Fitting these tractors with bull-dozers, angle-dozers, scrapers and so on, radically speeded up so many operations in this post-war period of reconstruction, so that the crawler tractor was seen as being a revolutionary new force in both agriculture and civil engineering. Beginning in 1948 a series of tracklayers, which included the TAK3 (track-layer agricultural kerosene) and TAD3 (track-layer agricultural diesel) and ITD3 (industrial track-layer diesel), began to make their appearance. Straight away they began making inroads into areas which had been formerly dominated by American manufacturers, but perhaps their greatest accolade was to beat the Yanks on their own

home ground, for they were widely employed in the construction of the new Alaskan Highway. The success of the company's crawlers, both industrial and agricultural, gave rise for even greater efforts on behalf of the marketing department and, as we discuss elsewhere, they came up with the 'master' concept for naming the various model types. So, in 1950, the crawlers became known as the Trackmaster, a designation which first appeared to the public at the Harrogate Convention that April. Two years later, the TAD6 and ITD6

Trackmaster dozer prototype

that the 30hp models were not up to the jobs that many contractors were expecting of them, and a proposal was made to up-rate them to a 40hp version and the first of these appeared early in 1960. However, due to the serious problems with the 900 series wheeled tractors that the company began to experience after they were introduced, a decision was taken not to immediately produce a crawler version but to defer production and see where things went.

The strive for increased power, however, was a major consideration for David Brown personally, and one day he announced that he felt that the company should have a 100hp crawler. In due course the order was passed down to Herbert Ashfield to implement, who writes, 'In the 1950's we were producing light agricultural crawler tractors at Browns, but sadly these had a fairly narrow market. The trouble seemed to be that the dealers (and the sales department for that matter), kept overselling them into the industrial market where the equipment required 40 horse power against the 30 horse power machines which we had available. Now we had attached to our sales office a new market research department which looked into the matter and recommended that, if we were to have any future in the crawler market, we should produce machines up to 100 horse power crawler capable of a top speed of 15 mph. We simply did not have the resources to tackle the top end of the market, but I set about producing a prototype and decided to go for a really big machine to show everybody just what they had let themselves in for. After choosing a Leyland engine, we decided on a fabricated frame as being easier to construct than castings. When we came to the tracks, the quickest solution seemed to be to have a double sprocket and have four links instead of two, enabling us to use DB existing parts. The steering would be clutch and brake. Having eventually completed the first machine, top management came and inspected it in the experimental fitting shop as the weather was bad. In the confines of the small shop, alongside 25 horse power agricultural tractors, it looked huge and its proportions frightened them to death; little wonder it became known to all concerned as Goliath! If mass production was to follow, it was declared that new machine and fitting shops would be required with bigger machine tools and heavier lifting equipment.

At this stage David Brown had now to be brought back into the picture. However, with a background of battle tank transmissions up to 700 horse power and marine transmissions for the navy running to several thousands of horse power, a mere hundred horse power crawler tractor looked very

David Brown 50 TD Tracklayer being loaded at Oban for transportation to the Isle of Barra for use in the film "Rockets Galore"

tracklayer came out with a six-cylinder diesel engine which produced a mean 50 horse power; it was offered with a choice of two track widths for either agricultural or industrial use. The following year it became known as the 50TD, as part of a new company designation scheme. This was a tractor that would stay in production until 1963 and see a total of 1,667 models being built. It was the company's first attempt with a 6-cylinder diesel engine, and as such it was to set a number of challenges for the firm's engineers, but it also gained many commendations and good reviews from outside sources. In 1953, with the introduction of the 30C and 30D wheeled tractors, the 30 series Tracklayers were introduced (these being the 30T, 30TD and 30ITD) and TAD6/ITD6 renamed as the 50TD/50ITD. Yet, despite their immediate success and total sales of 3,078 in the 30 series crawlers it was a fickle market and highly specialised as the demand for major improvements went marching on. Even so, it was evident that even the bigger tracklayers were being sold into heavy industrial applications which they were simply not suited for and the Service Department was facing a large number of requests for replacement clutches. The decision was therefore taken to examine the 50's clutch and gearbox to see where the problem lay, and as a result the Mk.II 50TD appeared in March 1957 with a larger diameter clutch, new running gear and a substantially strengthened set of side-plates which were fabricated from 1" thick sheet steel. A similar problem with 'clutch reliability' showed

The unique 100hp Tracklayer which never went into production

selling; in fact we were producing less and less, and more and more if you know what I mean. Our original agricultural Tracklayer had been designed for New Zealand, because that is where the demand was. In fact it was a very wide tractor which had a 64 inch track I think, I can't remember precisely now, but it was very wide and you couldn't turn it over. It was well appreciated in New Zealand, because it was very steep and hilly and the thing would slide sideways before it would turn over. It also sold well into farming areas where they had heavy clay which was obviously a good market. The big problem with our crawler was the fact that it was only a thirty horse-power Tracklayer; all the equipment dozers etc. which we had, were designed for the DB4 which was over forty horse power. Things were getting worse and worse, and people were saying that our crawlers were no good, but it was simply down to the fact that the dealers and users were asking too much of them. On one occasion I had to go to the United States to sort out this type of problem, because they were putting very large dozers on to relatively small tracklayers. When they tried to lift them, the dozer blades just stayed on the ground and the tracklayer's nose came up. It was quite a problem out there, because people were always overloading these

ordinary to him. He decided to view the beast on the Crosland Moor airfield, but in the vastness of the Pennine moors Goliath did not look half as big as it had in the fitting shop. David Brown looked at it with tacit approval and even smiled when Goliath rattled passed at speed. At this the boss flew back to London without comment and as Goliath took up a lot of space in the works, I decided to leave it on the moor. Meanwhile the production department went into the cost of the extra machinery and fitting shops required, if this crawler were to go into manufacture. These results confirmed my original contention that we just did not have the resources and even if we had, they could be more profitably applied to agricultural wheeled tractors. When the smoke cleared away, the inevitable decision had been reached and poor Goliath had no future so it spent its days being used as a dynamometer up at the airfield where it was eventually scrapped.' Various experimental tracklayers followed the 30, 40 and 50 series, including the DB5 of which 11 were built. The 990T offered the promise of a modern tracklayer for continuing production well into the 1960s, but this was not to be as Herbert Ashfield continues: 'As we entered the 1960s the tracklayers were becoming a really big problem for us, because at this point in time we were producing far too many models and variations for the quantity we were

990T Tracklayer prototype on Meltham Moor

machines, asking them to do work they just weren't designed for. We had a lot of trouble with some of the dealers, particularly those who were fairly small outfits; many were ready to make a sale at any cost, so they'd fit anything to them. We should have really designed our own dozers from the start although, in fact, we did ultimately do just that, but until we did we had a lot of problems in this regard. The 50TD six cylinder crawler was less of a problem, and it sold very well in South America so we asked our dealers out there why this particular tracklayer sold so well; in reply they said "well, its big and red and noisy!" It was obvious by the 'sixties that the demand for wheeled tractors was insatiable and we were making a profit on these, but we were making a loss on the tracked versions. Indeed these were a very difficult thing to produce, because our customers wanted industrial versions, wide versions, narrow versions etc., in fact you name it they wanted it. Ultimately, when Jack Thomson became Managing Director, we had a major inquest on the whole lot of our models. We were clearly over-extending our resources in so many ways and something had to give if were to make an efficient organisation, so we went out of Tracklayers and concentrated entirely on wheeled tractors.' Tom Lazenby recalls a similar series of events, saying; 'There were two things that really happened in the crawler market; first of all we were casting our net a bit too far with the crawlers, because we'd originally gone into this to try and meet a demand from Australia and New Zealand, where there was a great need for crawler tractors on steep terrain or in countryside where the roads might be hundreds or thousands of miles apart. We could supply that market, and similarly the areas of Britain where they had really hard clay-

The DB5 Prototype Tracklayer Left alongside a DB50 ITD

type soils, a light crawler was just right for these conditions, but we couldn't get to touch the big makers like Caterpillar. If we'd stayed at our area of speciality, just supplying a tracked version of our wheeled tractors we would have been alright, but it was entry to the industrial market which made things most difficult. Having failed to recognise our limitations, we made our second mistake and went on to try and compete with the big firms, our industrial division (at Feltham) were selling our machines into applications where they were simply too light and [as mentioned above] overloading them with equipment which they were never designed to carry.' So in 1963, almost to the 21st birthday of the commencement of the DB4, the company went out of crawler production altogether. For some it was just a natural part of the process of progression and concentration on the firm's strong points, but one wonders how the 990T or possibly a 1010T might have performed had they been fully developed and put into service with a complimentary range of associated equipment. At one stage, after the new assembly line opened at Meltham Mills, I was asked to do a costing exercise for the up-dating of the old assembly line for the production of special industrial wheeled and crawler tractors. The capital costs were not high, but they came at a time when the company were facing a very uncertain future just after a crippling strike by our draughtsmen. As far as I know the industrial assembly line plans died as a consequence, and within a very short time we were sold to the American multi-national Case.

A Trackmaster 50hp model with protective cab

Chapter 7
Taskmaster
1948 - 1965

There was such a demand for the industrial tractors, that David Brown's had converted from the Air Ministry tractors, that the firm decided to adapt the VAK1C (or Cropmaster as it had become known) into its own purpose-designed industrial tractor. It was a much simpler job than the Air Ministry conversions, and they ran this industrial version of the Cropmaster under the name Taskmaster until 1953. Its primary application was as an industrial towing tractor, and as such it featured heavy duty steering, wide mudguards and towing hitch; many were also provided with heavy duty winches. The company used several around their own works at Penistone, Lockwood and of course Meltham Mills. One of these tractors was regularly paired with a purpose-built servicing unit which incorporated a fuel tank and

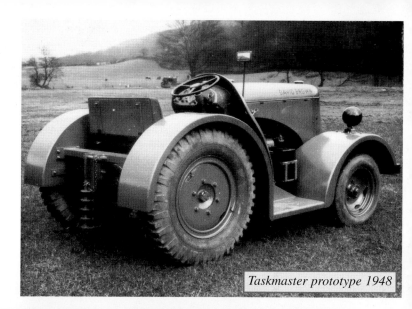

Taskmaster prototype 1948

The works' own Taskmaster and bowser in Meltham Mills Road

delivery system, battery charger/electric starter and an air-compressor. It was used to start up tractors that were awaiting despatch and which had stood in store alongside the football and cricket fields at the bottom of Meltham Mills Road. It was also used for recovering or restarting tractors which had failed whilst being taken up Meltham Mills Road and the Knowle on their primary road tests. As such this tractor often spent long periods of time parked just outside our house, and on more than one occasion I had the chance to drive the tractor on one of its 'rescue' jobs. Other well-known industrial users of the Taskmaster included Rolls Royce, Swan-Hunter, Commer Motors, and a large number of local authorities, including Halifax Borough Council who had placed an order for twelve cab-versioned models. Appearing as the VIGAR for the petrol engine version and VIDAR as the diesel, some 500 Taskmasters were made in the period up to 1953. It is jumping ahead of the rest of the story somewhat to discuss the engine changes which came about later in the David Brown story, but as these innovations came about, the Taskmaster was progressively fitted with 30, 900 and 950 engine units and corresponding tin-work on the bonnet/engine covers. Even so the same low styling, with heavy duty mudguards and bench seat was retained, and the family traits of the Taskmaster were continued through a succession of new tractors. In all some 2,752 Taskmasters were produced, with many and varied adaptations being made to suit industrial requirements all around the world. One of the most unusual variants was a fork-lift truck built for the Australian market, which had a back-to-front driving position with the engine unit behind the driver and the fork-lift to the front of this and situated between the small rear wheels.

Turbo Taskmaster with shunting attachment and cab 1956

Super Taskmaster with twin rear wheels 1957

Chapter 8
Aircraft Towing Tractors 1953 - 1956

As will be recalled David Brown's involvement with aircraft towing tractors began back in 1940 with the Air Ministry Tracklayer, which was hardly the most auspicious of starts. However, by the time the company ceased production of its successor in the 1950s, the firm's reputation had been considerably enhanced. As Herbert Ashfield remembers 'We kept on with the wheeled Air Ministry tractors until long after the war, and it was always a source of pleasure to me when I was on a flight that the towing tractor would invariably be an old David Brown, even abroad. The last ones were made in 1958 but these lasted well into the sixties, and many even longer.' The story of the Cropmaster variant, which appeared as the Taskmaster, has already been told, but the success of these highly-dependable low-geared tractors was sufficient in its own right to justify the full confidence which the Ministry of Defence placed in the company. Yet, added to this came the bonus that here was an all-British tractor, which was another major plus point in those cold war days of the early 1950s. 'It was an area which bred its own success' recalls Tom Lazenby, 'we did a lot of Ministry work for all branches of the armed forces, from towing heavy prototype planes at Farnborough to producing towing tractors for use on aircraft carriers.'

The first of the new generation of heavy towing tractors appeared in late 1952, when three prototype versions were produced for the Ministry of Defence; naturally they were allocated to the three main branches of the armed forces, with one each going to the Royal Air Force, the Royal Navy's Fleet Air Arm, and the Royal Corps of Engineers for evaluation. They were a development of the Taskmaster, but they incorporated a number of features which had been demanded by the users, including an improved winch and featured the engine unit which was to appear in the David Brown 30 series tractors. This development saw the creation of a new aircraft towing tractor available in two engine types - the diesel version being the 30ID and the petrol being the 30IC. A large number of these were purchased for the Royal Air Force and the Fleet Air Arm and these also incorporated special Ministry requirements. Turbo models were also produced, as were twin rear wheel versions and medium wheeled towing tractors. According to Leonard Craven's summary of tractor production, in total 320 aircraft towing tractors were built in the period leading up to October 1958 when the 950 variant came out.

RAF towing tractors on the test route, Knowle Lane, Meltham

Prince Charles drives a Royal Navy towing tractor aboard HMS Eagle in 1956

Towing tractors with the giant Brabazon aircraft

Chapter 9
DB25 & DB30 Series
1953 - 1958

By the early 1950's it became clear that the "Cropmaster" range of tractors, whilst still selling well, were beginning to face fierce competition from other manufacturers who were undercutting David Brown's list price. It was also clear that a new breed of tractor owner was emerging and, whereas the immediate post-war demand had been for bigger and heavier tractors of 30 hp or more, there was now a growing trend to lighter tractors of 20 to 25 hp. This was probably brought about because smaller farms, especially those which had not mechanised in the 1940s, were now finding it was time to do so. To continue to farm with only horse-power was now becoming very uneconomical, and the smaller farms quickly began to convert - even those in very marginal upland areas. Thankfully new grant regimes assisted the poorer farmers to increase food production in post-war Britain, and it was greatly needed due to the various food shortages, especially the meat ration which had

DB 25 prototype in 1952 with Cropmaster tin-work

been dramatically cut by 1950. Now, whilst the Cropmaster was simply the best post-war tractor on the market, Ford, Massey and a number of other manufacturers began to realise that there was this growing market for smaller tractors, and it was a niche that the Ferguson models very quickly began to exploit. If the Cropmaster was going to compete, it was clearly evident that it would require radical new features in order to prolong its life. So the decision was taken to produce a stripped down version of the Cropmaster range, where certain economies of manufacturing could be passed on to the customer. One of the most obvious solutions was to produce a tractor with a smaller engine, and with a 25hp version immediate reductions could be made in the selling price. Meanwhile, economies in the manufacture of a 30hp version could also be achieved through careful design. As Leonard Craven told me; 'In the early 1950s, as the post-war reconstruction period came to an

DB25 Pre-production model

DB25 with Common Toolbar as Spring Tine Cultivator opposite Meltham Mills School field

end, the demand for tractors continued apace but the availability of supplies was much more widespread. In turn this depressed the agricultural market slightly, and after a decade of being able to sell anything and everything they made, tractor manufacturers found that prices were now becoming an important issue with many farmers. David Brown were no exception and the firm decided to produce the stripped down version of the Cropmaster.' Fitted with fan-type fenders, single seats, the models became known as the 25 and 30 series tractors. In recalling their introduction, Herbert Ashfield writes 'Ferguson came in with real mass production with Massey Ferguson, and later on Ford got going as well so we began to feel the draft a bit. My contention was that we should stop somewhere in between the 25 horse power Ferguson and the 40 horse power Ford. Unfortunately the problem with the Cropmaster and the Super Cropmaster was that it was getting as pricey as the Ford and farmers were getting less power for their money. So we did a strip down version, the 25 and 30 which were wonderful tractors, just right for British farmers. We easily undercut Ford, with a very modern tractor and at the same time produced a superior tractor to

The 1000th production DB25

DB30 Prototype with Tri-disc plough in 1953

An experimental high-clearance 30D with mid-mounted tool bar. Designed for the Californian market in 1954 but never put into production.

the Ferguson. They were designated by Mr. David Brown as 25 and 30, which signified their nominal horse-power. He had decided that his name should figure large in the tractor's image, and that the 'master' name detracted from the image of quality he felt the firm's name warranted. So out went the 'Cropmaster' name, and David Brown came to the fore - but we were soon put at a disadvantage as a number of makers weren't as scrupulous in their designation numbers as we were, and added another five or even ten horse-power on to their designation number, giving customers entirely the wrong impression.'

The 25 and 30 series were one of Meltham's greatest secrets, and although some books and magazines have commented that the tractors went on sale in February 1953, we can put the record straight and state categorically that they were not released to the public until Friday 27th March when they went on show at the Harrogate Convention. At this event David Brown dealers

and distributors were presented with the DB25, 30C and 30D. Other dealers were invited to the factory to view the new models and in the inset picture above Mr. Tom Lazonby shows Mr. Tom Norton owner of the Automobile Palace Ltd. (DB dealers in Wales) a model 25 as it comes off the production line.

The 25 (later to be known as the 25C) represented David Brown's entry into the popular priced class, and was presented in such a way as to immediately appeal to both the small and the large-scale farmer. Powered by the 3.5" bore petrol or petrol/paraffin engine, it was fitted with a 6-speed gearbox and the latest two-position hydraulic lift, the 25 brought 'Cropmaster' performance and reliability within reach of those who could not hitherto afford it. For a comparatively low initial outlay the small farmer could now purchase a powerful, but economical tractor, which would be capable of every job on the farm. The thoughtful consideration that the farmer could continue to use his own trailed implements in conjunction with the decent drawbar on the 25 was well appreciated. This allowed him to mechanise his operations, and not be tied down to the immediate expenditure of purchasing mounted implements. It was a big difference, and it made the 25 a firm favourite with both the farming press and the small-scale farmers who bought it. Another feature was the Traction Control Unit, TCU which was a controlled weight transfer system and enabled even small tractors such as the 25 to carry out heavy work with large implements. As mentioned earlier, the 25 also appealed to larger farms, because of its low-price to high-performance factors making it a suitable choice for a general duty machine. Some farms purchased the single pan-seat 25 as a second machine, others sold their larger tractors and standardised on a small fleet of 25hp tractors. The appearance of the 30 horse-power tractor in its stripped down version was also well appreciated, although at this time it did not look greatly different from the Cropmaster. Indeed, as one of our pictures show, the original 30 was fitted with Cropmaster tin-work and badged as such. However, the new 30, in both its engine configurations, was a remarkably economic tractor achieving a very high acreage per hour to low fuel consumption ratio. The change to a styling similar to the 25, incidentally came about a year after the introduction of the 30, and with this the famous DB bench seat finally disappeared from the standard market. Mind you, I recall that well into the 1970s some of our tractors for the European market, especially Germany and Belgium, were still calling for bench seats and square-topped wide mud-guards on which people could sit as well.

DB30 Half-track model

Rear view of DB30 pulling Tri-disc MkII plough in 1953

Chapter 10
VAD6 50D
1953 - 1959

At the beginning of 1953 another new product came out from the company, in the shape of the Cropmaster 50. It had been the long-held dream of David Brown to make a 6-cylinder diesel capable of producing 50 horse power, and with this model it was hoped to provide a tractor which could break into, and then capture the top end of the agricultural and industrial market. It was an ambitious concept, and it owed its origins to the 50 hp crawler tractor of 1952 rather than the 30 hp Cropmaster. Initially designated the VAD6, the name Cropmaster 50 was employed more as a marketing concept, rather than specifically conveying the actual pedigree of the tractor. After it began rolling off the production line in January, its initial market was aimed specifically at the company's export trade.

In the grounds of David Brown's house, the first DB50 is seen at Durker Roods, Meltham.

It was envisaged that it would satisfy a demand for countries where tractors were needed to pull large trailers, specifically in South America and the developing countries of the Commonwealth. The first major public appearance of this large towing tractor in Britain was at the Harrogate Convention in April 1953, but by this time it had already undergone a sea-change and been renamed as the 50D.

I asked Herbert Ashfield to explain why the tractor had come about, as it seemed to be so much at odds with the company's stated policy of the day. He told me; 'The idea for the 50D came about because a lot of people in the organisation were saying we wanted a big wheeled tractor that was like a powerful crawler and fitted with a big 6-cylinder engine. So we made a big engine and a transmission that was rugged enough to stand up to it, and on this power unit we developed the TAD6 crawler and then the VAD6 wheeled tractor. It was designed basically from scratch, and it wasn't related to any of the others; in fact it was more closely related to the early DB4 tracklayers than it was

A prototype VAD6 now named as a Cropmaster Diesel Fifty, in 1949

to the Cropmaster. However, neither of these machines ever sold in quantity because a) we couldn't produce enough and b) the export market was a bit dodgy! In fact, we were selling more overseas than we were in this country, and its always a bad policy to have a machine who's primary market is an export one.

The trouble with an export market is you can't easily cure problems which develop with the equipment; but if you have a good home market, you can sort out the teething troubles on your own doorstep. The 50D sold quite well in South Africa, Australia and South America, in fact anywhere where there was a requirement for hauling big four wheel trailers. The main thing that was wrong with the original 6-cylinder engine was its cylinder head, in that it was a single head. Because of this it used to warp quite badly and you'd blow the gasket between the cylinders if you overloaded the engine. It was a common fault, and it wasn't really overcome until the 1970s when I devised an arrangement which employed two 3-cylinder cylinder heads on the 6-cylinder block.' The 50D was quite unlike any other David Brown wheeled tractor, as it had no hydraulics, a side-mounted belt pulley and a 4-speed PTO. Its 6-cylinder engine was, like the Cropmaster, a $3^5/8$" Bore and a 4" stroke, and it used many components that were employed in the Cropmaster engine, however it was not an uprated Cropmaster engine as some commentators have stated. It was a high, rugged tractor with a good bench seat, but it could hardly be called handsome. Its headlamps, particularly those mounted on stalks which gave an elevated position above the radiator grill gave it an ungainly appearance. It was the same with those models which had the air-cleaner mounted in a higher than normal position, and thus imparted a less than aesthetic look to the tractor. Big, powerful and rugged it may have been, but it was not a popular model and in total only 1,260 were produced before construction was brought to an end in the summer of 1958. The market for a 6-cylinder in this country had not yet developed sufficiently for the company to maintain its confidence in the product and develop it for a wider UK application, but it would come again with the 1200 series.

Again, Herbert Ashfield provides another insight into the 6-cylinder engine's demise, noting 'I felt we should go on with a 6-cylinder and bring out a big tractor for the 1960s, but we would have had to make substantial improvements on our existing design. Unfortunately it was the cost of both tooling and the re-designing of the tractor which killed that one, so out went the 6-cylinder idea. These development costs were so high that the management wouldn't pay for them, but even so they wanted a more powerful tractor. Over the years I'd been planning ways that we could achieve this by turbo charging, but we could never get a turbo charger that could give the life we required so we continued on with a four-cylinder engine and waited for someone to come up with what we needed.' Accordingly the 50D went out of production and the 6-cylinder DB Tractor came to an end for the meantime, yet the 50D itself has become a much sought after collector's piece thanks to its rarity!

Rear view of a VAD6 prototype with trailed rotavator in 1949

Experimental 50D tricycle tractor at Durker Roods, Meltham 1953

VAD6 Prototype on steel rear wheels 1949

Chapter 11
900 Series 1955 - 1957

Sadly, this model has often been quoted as David Brown's worst tractor, and it is true that it did earn itself quite a reputation. Yet, from the outset, it had been intended that the 900 should only be a stop-gap measure, an interim tractor, before the firm began producing a tractor which would be suited to fast-advancing mechanisation in the agricultural world. Simultaneous with the introduction of the David Brown 900, came the time when the company began a new way in designating its various models. As we mentioned earlier, the DB25 & DB30 delivered that level of horse-power, and a bit more, but some manufacturers were not as scrupulous and their model numbers were marginally higher than the actual horse-power which the tractors delivered. David Browns were not prepared to indulge in this practice, even though it obviously influenced customers to buy certain types of tractor. The outcry which came about when tractors failed to deliver the purported horse-power, subsequently led to the establishment of National Tractor Testing. The Marketing Department at Meltham Mills came up with the idea that they should use a designation which in no way could be construed as horse-power, and because of this they devised the 900 numbering series.

In 1954 David Browns began experimenting with a new prototype, in which it intended to embody all the features needed to up-date the Cropmaster and its stripped down 25 and 30 successors. This was to be a completely new tractor, and it was known as the VAD5. Herbert Ashfield drew once more on his recollections when I asked him how this came about; 'From around 1954-5, there was pressure for an entirely new design

Production model 900 with hedge trimmer

SWX 833

of tractor as the Cropmaster was supposed to be a bit dated. It must have been when it was a bit flat at the works, as I was commissioned to design a basically new tractor. One of the things we had trouble with was the cast-iron frame, which was originally cast in just one piece; and, as there were only two foundries in the country that could cast it, we had real trouble in getting supplies at times. I talked this problem through with our Chief Designer, and we decided that the frame could be chopped in half and made in two pieces, which would (in turn) make it easier for small foundries to cast it. But this was only a temporary measure, and the idea which someone put forward was to copy the Fordson Major and have a steel sub-frame on which we could easily mount the engine and gain more flexibility in manufacture. However, as things turned out, it never worked out that way, but we did make various prototypes to test the idea. Another thing we wanted to do was get rid of the type of steering rod which we had used since the early days, so we made up a model with the steering over the top. It looked very American when it was finished, and it too never went into production. However, a lot of the ideas behind the VAD5 were ultimately incorporated in production of the 900. For example, we found that we could get the same features as we had in the existing line, by using the same castings and engine mounts etc. When we came to the actual prototype of the 900, we also had a large number of new features which we wanted to incorporate, including: An adjustable heavy duty front axle which would give better steering geometry on the wider track widths; Live power take off shaft and power lift pump able to keep running when the tractor was stopped; Weight transfer from implement to tractor rear wheels, namely traction control, which would prevent wheel spin under heavy

VAD5 Prototype 1954 never went into production, but some features were incorporated in the 900

loads; Differential lock; Hydraulic depth control for use with mounted implements lacking depth wheels; Comfort seat (instead of the pan seat fitted to 25 and 30 series); Revised styling and a dual colour scheme; Batteries positioned each side of the seat or in front of radiator; A repositioned air cleaner in front of radiator (inside the bonnet) instead of allowing it to hang externally on the side of the engine; and last, but by no means least, a distributor injection pump on diesel engines which was intended to be cheaper, smaller and give smoother running. Not all these features were incorporated in the 900, and due to its short life, some of the improvements were actually carried over into the 950 or 990.'

During its launch at the Smithfield Show Mr. David Brown junior, said 'Our policy must always be to give value for money - that is something about which we, as Yorkshiremen, are very particular - and we are convinced that the 900 tractor upholds that tradition. With its twin range gear box giving 6 forward and 2 reverse gears, a 2-speed PTO and pulley, improved one-piece bonnet styling, overload release, independent foot brakes and Traction Control Unit it seemed to give really good value for money. This was particularly pleasing when it was revealed that its ex-works price was just £593 10s (£593.50p), a snip at £42 10s (£42.50p) less than the 30D. Providing extra output with greater economy, it should have been the tractor for the mid-50s, but it was sadly not to be. Unfortunately, the 40hp 900 got off to a very bad start due to its new distributor injection pump, made by CAV, that was fitted to all diesel models. Although prototypes had been thoroughly tested, production pumps were prone to seizure. This was ultimately found to be due to the use of a different (probably cheaper) steel for the pump plungers and body. Tom Lazenby recalls how the matter gave his sales department a major headache until it was finally resolved. 'The fuel pump on the 900 frightened us to death because of all the troubles it gave but we couldn't revert back to the in-line pump, because this couldn't work on the 900 and although we still had the 25s and 30s in production, all we were building at the time were 900s. Things very nearly came to a full stop. The way things were going it could have ended in a spectacular law suit with CAV, and probably would have done if it hadn't been for an incident which transpired on Huddersfield station. Obviously we were trying hard to find what was wrong and so were CAV. Pumps were going up and down between Meltham and the CAV factory, going by rail, by wagon, by everything just as they were coming back to us from overseas by air and by sea for re-servicing. We just couldn't get the things to work, so we sent them back to the makers to see if they could. Oddly enough, CAV could get them to work again, but don't ask me how; yet when they came back to us then they began to fail again. As the situation worsened, the Service Department were under so much pressure to get tractors moving right across Europe that they had to rob those coming in for the assembly line. In fact, after a while they had got so many pumps out of the line, that there weren't enough engines going through to keep production going. By this time the night shift was lucky if it had half the pumps it needed to get it through to the morning. Well you can't go on making engines without pumps because you can't leave them to be fitted afterwards as the complete engine assemblies had to be tried on the test-bed. The strange thing was, the pumps that were being fitted would work on the engine test-bed, and they didn't fail

The next stage was the VAD5G Prototype which has lost the American look and now resembles the 900

By 1955 the prototype 900 has emerged!

Production 900 with the pulverisor version of a forage harvester near Meltham Gas Works

when the finished tractor was tested up and down the Knowle, it was afterwards when they failed - usually when they began their working lives. We couldn't understand this, nor could CAV. Then, one night, we had an incident at Huddersfield station and it all became clear.

Because of the acute shortage of pumps, CAV were managing to make sufficient one day to meet our production needs the next, but because they were so urgently needed they had to send these up by passenger train. We used to send a van down to meet these trains coming in from the Birmingham area that were carrying a box full of pumps; almost invariably the train would have a box full of pumps on, sometimes two boxes of pumps or even more. I don't know how big these boxes were, but one night, either the man in the train threw them out or they were dropped on the station platform with a quite a bang! Our driver suddenly guessed that this could be what was causing the problem, so he brought them directly round to the Engine Test Department, and we put them straight on to test. None of them worked at all! So what was happening to make the pumps fail if they were dropped or banged? Well our engineers began to take a closer look at these pumps, and what they found was this. When they built the units CAV had used a component inside the pump and somehow, during the machining of it, it had built up stress. However, when you dropped them or put the pumps into regular service, it relieved the stress, the component jammed and the pump failed. Within days of making this revelation, we were out of trouble with that, but our reputation had taken an awful battering.' Herbert Ashfield continues the story, 'David Brown's were relatively lucky, because on our engines the pump coupling key sheared and we only needed a new pump; on some other makes of engine, the timing gears stripped and the valves went through the piston crowns

necessitating a new engine. CAV did a campaign change on all their pumps but this did nothing to increase the 900's popularity.'

Another problem noted in the 900 was found with the steering, especially after the safety authorities introduced a limit on the amount of play at the steering wheel rim and applied it enthusiastically to tractors. Herbert Ashfield once again picks up the account: 'The limit was about 2" I believe, but the 900 seemed to develop 2½ and stay there, so several new steering relay lever bearings had to be fitted to maintain compliance with this requirement. The plan to install a comfort seat was dropped around this time and, while this no doubt kept the price down, it was not a feature that could be used by the salesman as a talking point. Then, in late 1957 a live power take off and power lift pump were introduced and this kept sales going aided by the superior performance of the machine over the old "Cropmaster" range.' In 1958 Brown's decided to not make any further improvements to the 900, and instead they designed the other outstanding features into the new model it was proposing, thereby making a clean break with the past. Thus, while the 25s and 30s were still being produced, the 900 went out of production prematurely in the summer of 1958 and it was superseded by the 950 which was free of teething troubles and enjoyed a good reputation from the word go. With the Livedrive versions which became an option during production run, a total of 13,770 of the 900s were produced, including a small batch of tractors designated as 903 (a row-crop version for the Californian market) but still bearing a 900 badge. However, when the last of the blue-wheeled tractors was taken on a test run down Meltham Mills Road for the final time, there were more than a few people who were relieved to see the back of them.

Chapter 12
VAD12
2D Series
1956 - 1961

One of the most unusual tractors ever built at Meltham Mills was the David Brown VAD12/V or 2D (as it was better known), which entered production in 1956 and lasted until 1961. This was a very small, lightweight tractor which featured a 2-cylinder 14 BHP air-cooled diesel engine which had been specially designed by David Brown's, and had a mid-mounted tool carrier which carried a range of implements.

To tell the story of how the 2D was developed I enlisted the assistance of Derek Marshall (the current chairman of the David Brown Tractor Club) and, once again, Herbert Ashfield who writes about its development. 'The sales director, Fred Marsh, cherished the idea of a low cost, 14 to 16 horse-power tractor which he believed would sell to the small farmer still using animals. As a basis for our design I looked at the Massey Harris "Pony" tractor of orthodox design which met the specification but it did not perform well under test, and so this particular project was stillborn. The Sales Director, however, did not give up easily and he bought an Allis Chalmers model "G" for us to inspect. This was a twelve horse power tool frame tractor with the engine at the rear, tools in the middle and a hand lift. The driver sat in front of the engine and behind the tools. "It must have a power lift, it must be able to plough, and turn on its own length" said Mr. Marsh as he rapidly outlined requirements which, while making it superior to the "G", would also make it more expensive. His eloquence, however, carried management with him and I was directed to produce a specification and design for such a tractor. When we tested the "G", we found it suitable for light cultivation only, its biggest problem was its petrol engine which stalled very easily. Another limitation was the excessive effort required to operate the hand lift, so we decided on a power lift. Being currently plagued by oil leaks on our standard hydraulic system, I opted for a pneumatic lift which, I decided, could leak all it wanted. Doubts were also expressed on a mid-mounted plough. "You can't push a plough!" seemed to be a fairly general opinion but we did not intend to

The Prototype 2D with the Ford 10hp engine seen at Meltham Hall

push it, rather we pulled it from the front axle. We then produced a functional prototype to try out our basic suppositions using a 10hp Ford car engine which, apart from stalling easily, performed satisfactorily.

The engine became our next problem. Because of being rear mounted, it overhung the back axle and any out of balance force resulted in excessive vibration. Small multi-cylinder engines such as the Ford car engine were acceptable as regards vibration but unacceptable because they stalled easily under varied loading. Small diesels which were available in the required power range were too much out of balance and indeed almost threw the driver out of his seat. I therefore decided we must build our own perfectly balanced 2-cylinder diesel with a heavy flywheel to avoid stalling. However, we adopted an unorthodox approach, because the reciprocating 'out of balance' force created by a piston can only be perfectly balanced by a similar reciprocating force 180^0 out of phase. To achieve this we put the pistons in line and balanced them by a dummy piston in between and opposite, thus 180^0 out of phase. The engine ran smoothly, beyond our expectations and we had no further trouble with vibration, but to simplify the installation, we designed the engine to be air cooled.

It met our requirements in the field. It would not stall and could be run at low speed in high gear for light work - above all, from a sales point of view it was very practical because the fuel consumption was extremely low. Sales of production tractors started slowly. The machine was viewed with caution by the farming community. On the other hand, the academic institutions both home and abroad, were loud in their praise for the revolutionary layout.' However, despite this great accolade, the tractor went through some difficult teething problems before it could be marketed, as Derek Marshall reveals 'When the field tests began in earnest, we started with what was still a very basic unit as the engine and transmission units were not ready at this early stage. Consequently, as the first mock-up used for trial was devoid of the two main power units, the prototype was pulled along by another tractor. At first sight this might appear to be rather pointless but, to the contrary, this provided valuable information and data which enabled us to make changes and improvements to the linkage geometry and steering even at this early stage. In view of the unique design and specification, it was intended to keep the project as secret and as far away from prying eyes as possible although it was inevitable that locals and casual observers could see what was going on. However, we were obviously quite pleased at the secrecy of the exercise, even though we were sure that questions were asked about the sanity of two or three grown-up people dragging this weird object up and down the fields for no apparent purpose or results. When the Ford engine was fitted the machine ran under its own power, and more meaningful tests could begin. During these tests two major problems arose and it became clear that these would need addressing before production could begin. Firstly, controlling the hand-lift mechanism with the implement attached, (despite the adjustable balance springs) required a Herculean effort on the part of the operator. Whilst lowering the implement was not too bad, once it touched the ground, it was then necessary to overcome the full resistance of the springs in order to provide the required working depth. As this was almost an impossibility, we considered it was essential to provide some power assistance to the lift, and this was achieved very successfully by fitting a small compressed air pump. This we mounted directly to the front of the gear-box and pressure was fed to the tubular main frame which, when suitably adapted, provided an excellent air tank for the system. Secondly, depth control of the implement was still somewhat erratic, particularly with the long tool-bar or cultivator; a condition which appeared to be due to the fact that the two lift ropes controlling the depth (and being attached centrally to the tool-bar) allowed it to 'yaw' or see-saw. Fitting a small depth wheel at the outer ends of the tool-bar, overcame this problem, and also provided a more accurate control of the working depth.

It soon became evident that the engine was well able to provide ample power, even under the most severe conditions but, once again, two fundamental problems had to be solved. The inertia start system as a unit worked reasonably well, but difficulties arose however under cold start conditions when the engine invariably failed to pick up before the inertia unit wound down; in turn this required the operator to continue frantically cranking to effect a start. As the starting problems continued, a major (and much welcomed) change was made at this point with the development and introduction of a full electric system, including starter, alternator and full

Long wheelbase 2D 1954

Short wheelbase 2D at Scar Bottom Mills 1955

PWX 503

Experimental front-engined 2D at Lee Mills, Scholes.

Short wheelbase industrial model 2D at Scar Bottom

lighting. We considered this to be a necessary requirement, and we were delighted with the satisfactory and meaningful tests which resulted in only a few alterations or changes being required.' The old hank winding shed at Meltham Mills, had meanwhile been converted to a special assembly line for the 2D, and production began shortly after the tests were completed. The tractor made its first public appearance at the Smithfield Show in December 1955 where it was promoted as 'A multi-purpose machine to work on any farm or horticultural holding.'

In total some 2,008 were produced, with a large variety of special models appearing in short and long wheel-bases, wide or narrow widths, low or high clearance models, and even one which had the look of a small conventional tractor. It was widely praised by various universities and agricultural colleges, and the farming press called it 'the tractor of the future'. However, as the 1960s dawned, it became clear that the sales targets were not being achieved. I asked Herbert Ashfield why this was, and he recalls; 'The 2D never sold in the quantities originally forecast, but we were receiving orders for all sorts of modified machines which only sold in small quantities to specialist markets and incidentally with a profit margin which took no account of the extra overheads incurred in producing them. Admittedly, it was very popular in places and we sold a lot in Holland, France and around the market gardens near London. For example, it sold well because you could plough right up to the hedge bottom but its enemy was always the second-hand tractor. It was when it was sold to a big farm that the troubles began, because the farmer wanted all sorts of elaborate equipment, hoes etc. Sadly the 2D never really took off as David Brown and Fred Marsh imagined it would, even though all the institutions and universities said this was the tractor of the future. Then in 1961 the Managing Director, Jack Thomson, instituted an enquiry in to the question of why they weren't selling. So I looked at it very coolly and the first thing I did was to ask how many salesmen they had trying to sell standard tractors and how many were selling 2Ds. I found out it was taking about three times the salesman hours to sell a 2D as opposed to that taken to clinch a deal on a standard tractor because operators had to be convinced to use the tractor. So, talking to both my field test personnel and farmers, I found that many users were wanting a rear mounted linkage and they were buying small second-hand tractors. This meant that the enemy of the 2D was the second-hand Fordson, Ferguson and David Brown, so if the farmer could buy a good used tractor for about the same as they were paying for a new 2D, he would probably go for a machine with rear-mounted linkage. This set us thinking, could we produce a small standard tractor at a reasonable price? So we got all the figures out and looked at the profit margin on the 2Ds, and these showed us that if you took the standard overheads you were making a profit on the 2D, but when you added all the extras such as extra salesman hours and whatnot you were actually making a loss. So out went the 2D and in came the 880s and later we developed the 770 which we did in narrow and low-clearance versions and this took over a lot of the 2D's functions. This was a really superb lightweight tractor of conventional design and relatively low enough in price for the small farmer and it could therefore compete with the second-hand 30 horse-power tractors from Ford and Ferguson.'

Chapter Number 13
950 Series 1958 - 1961

VAD 11 Prototype at Scar Bottom Mills with tin-work showing a styling ten years ahead of this 1958 view.

As we have already shown, the 900 only ran three years, and rather than completely replacing the DB25's and 30's it was produced alongside them until they also finished in 1958. Meanwhile the 950 started production in that year; so the company concurrently had three main models running together, a rather chaotic situation for both the production and sales teams. Production of the 950 began on Monday 28th October 1958, but it was decided to wait for the turn of the year to announce the launch and, for marketing reasons, not to do it at the Smithfield Show. Accordingly, with the awkwardness of the 900 behind them, and having seen what other manufacturers had already done with their 'tractors for the 1960s' it was David Brown's turn for a two venue launch. These launch celebrations were carried out on opposite sides of the world, with David Brown senior performing his launch at the Canadian Farm & Industrial Trade Fair in Toronto, and his son presiding over a DB function in Harrogate. This launch took place on 28th January 1959, and it presented what was apparently a completely new design. In reality it was the Mk.II 900, and it embodied all the features which David Brown had intended to put into that

model had it not had such a disastrous start in life!

The 950's principle features, and all of them standard, were: An exceptionally easy steering unit with a very small turning circle; high ground clearance; full road and field lighting (with a rear-mounted floodlight); screw-type lift rod and geared levelling lever; adjustable front and rear wheel widths (from 52" to 76" in 4" steps); fully adjustable drawbar; universal linkage for category one or two implements; new type gear pump; large 11.00 x 32 rear tyres; power take-off and belt pulley; simplified TCU to prevent wheel-spin; independent foot brakes; adjustable overload release; steering column throttle control; and (at last!) the 'Super-Comfortable Driving Seat'. Its $3\frac{5}{8}$" bore engine produced 42.5BHP, but extensive field tests had already proved its economy in operation. In addition there was also a 950 Livedrive model, with 'live' power take-off and a 'live' hydraulic system. Optional extras were power steering; three-way isolator valve providing instant selection of the main or two auxiliary services and a linkage drawbar for light towing duties.

It was a marvellous tractor, presented on a marvellous stand that had been based on the award winning display that the company had

Tom Lazenby shows the 950 during exhaust brake demonstrations at Knowle Lane in March 1960.

used at Smithfield the preceding month. At the official opening of the Toronto stand, Mr. David Brown was accompanied by his wife and four full-blooded Indian Chiefs and two Indian Princesses. After the ceremonies, these natives made David a full Chief of the Iroquois tribe, an honour which had been bestowed upon few English visitors - indeed, the previous personality to receive this accolade was Her Royal Highness Princess Margaret.

At the British launch, Mr. J. B. Townley, managing director of DB distributors Barton Motors (Preston) Ltd. Said 'We have seen today what I call a thundering good tractor, which represents a tremendous endeavour on the part of the David Brown company to present us with a fine product at a very competitive price. With this tractor we have really got something.' The farming press were just as enthusiastic about it, and one of the Canadian papers said 'The 950 is a triumph for David Brown. This little company from England have taken on the American giants and beaten them. The result is a new tractor that has come about because the company has been listening closely to its customers on farms all over the world. The result is a machine to suit all markets.'

Tom Lazenby remembers the introduction of the 950 with a great deal of pride, saying: 'The problems of the fuel pump and steering on the 900 gave us no end of trouble, and we lost a lot of customer confidence because of that. In the end it made us bring forward the 950 which was really the 900 with a bigger set of wheels which went up from 28s to 32s. It was a sort of Mark II 900, but it had a little bit more filling here and there. But, because it was the same tractor really, we had to make a lot of changes in how it looked and performed. Messrs Ashfield & Co in the Engineering Department had solved the problems of how the tractor worked, but we had

950 Implematic production model

the job of selling it, and we had all on to overcome the problems of customer confidence which the 900 had given us. We had to make a tractor which had instant sales appeal and get away from the blue colour which David Brown junior had chosen for the 900's wheels and radiator grill; so one Saturday morning five of us assembled at the works including the Managing Director Jack Thomson, George Shannon, Alan Walker and somebody from production. When we got there they had got a series of tractors lined up with different coloured wheels,

A line up of 950s awaiting despatch from Meltham Mills in 1960

including the yellow ones. After some consultation and debate we decided that the yellow ones best complimented the red livery, and Jack Thomson said 'Aye that'll do, we'll never pick that *#++!@ awful blue again!'

Herbert Ashfield recalls what happened next: 'Because of the problems with the 900 we went straight on to the 950, and this tractor incorporated all the improvements that we were going to put in the 900. The 950 was a cracker right from the word go, and it sold ever so well, in the end we made 5,574 of the 950 T & U Series, but it was the Implematic version which really did well. In all we sold 18,125 of the V and W, and A and B versions of the 950.' In December 1959 the company brought out a revolutionary development of the standard tractor, in the shape of the Implematic.'

The Implematic was, in many ways, a remarkable innovation, as it set about addressing a problem which farmers had been facing since the principle of mounting equipment on tractor linkages was first developed in the 1930s. For a long time manufacturers were divided on how the working depth of an implement should be controlled, some used a depth wheel whilst others employed a form of automatic draught control. Generally tractors were designed to operate one type of equipment or the other, but not both. This resulted in the poor farmer having his choice of equipment restricted, and it was a situation that remained deadlocked until David Brown introduced the Implematic. At the 1959 Smithfield Show the 950 Implematic (V and W versions) went on display, featuring an ingenious

modification to the hydraulic system which permitted the operation of dual implement types, plus differential lock - and all at no extra cost! Simplicity was the keynote of the new system, with a single lever controlling both the choice of implement type and the Traction Control Unit. To cater for implements without a depth wheel, Brown's introduced Traction Depth Control, an arrangement in which the top link was spring-loaded and, in work, was under compression from the draft forces acting on the implement. This compression of the top link actuated, via a Bowden cable, the movement of a hydraulic valve. For any given control lever setting, the implement goes into work until the set draft is achieved. When the ground conditions varied, the draft automatically increased or decreased, as did the pressure on the top link. In turn this caused the hydraulic valve to move; for example when the draft increased it allowed more oil to be pumped into the lift cylinder which raised the implement and then restored the draft to the pre-set level but when the draft decreased, oil was released from the cylinder thus allowing the implement to go deeper. This automatic regulation of the implement was occurring all the time it was in work, and thus saved considerable re-setting time and a lot of man hours. When the tractor was using implements with a depth wheel, the hydraulic system operated in exactly the same manner as before. With this feature the 950 became even more popular, and it soon erased the painful memories which the 900 had

bestowed and all concerned were hard pressed to cope with the demand. Indeed 1960 turned out to be a record year for the Meltham Mills works, and as David Brown junior said 'We are going to build more tractors at the Meltham factory than we have ever built before.' Yet this may have seemed an overly optimistic hope, especially in view of the fact that there was an overall 16% decrease in the sale of tractors in Britain that year. However, whilst other manufacturers were tightening their belts, David Brown went on to achieve his record output, and by February the despatch of tractors was a remarkable 50% up on the same period the previous year. Salesmen could not keep up with the demand, and all over the world farmers were having to wait for their new machines. Extra labour was recruited for Meltham and Leigh works, and by May the production had been dramatically increased. By September output had reached an all-time record, and 80% of production was going for export.

In the midst of this success, the 850 was launched and David Brown also entered into an agreement with the Oliver Corporation of America to make two types of tractors on their behalf, one of which (the model 600) is pictured inset. We will discuss the Oliver orders later, but before leaving the 950 we will mention that the final improvements to the model appeared as the A and B versions in October 1960 (in time for Smithfield) and these included additional refinements to what was already a 'world-beating tractor'.

Chapter Number 14
850 Series 1961 - 1965

Whilst the 950 was taking care of the main end of the market, David Browns remained conscious of the fact that a smaller tractor would have a ready appeal. As we have seen Jack Thompson, the Managing Director, had already decided to discontinue the 2D in the latter part of 1960 and secretly a decision had been taken to introduce a small 3-cylinder diesel tractor of conventional appearance in its stead. As Herbert Ashfield now writes 'As we came on with the 950, we began to look at the fact that there was a need for a smaller tractor. We decided to designate this the 850, and aim for between 30 and 35 horse-power. Obviously we needed a new power unit for this machine, and one of the things we looked at was the Perkins 3-cylinder engine. It influenced our thinking quite a lot, but having decided that a 3-cylinder engine was cheaper to make in smaller powers than a 4-cylinder we began to design our own 3-cylinder tractor to put in the 850.' However, it was to be some time before this unit was ready, and as the 2D was to be phased out, it was decided to bring in the 4-cylinder 3.5" bore engine producing 35 BHP into a dimensionally smaller version of the 950. Like its big brother, it was available in petrol (VAG2A model) and diesel (VAG2B model) forms, although these later gave way to the C and D variants in September 1961 when the 850 Implematic was given a new multi-speed pto. At the same time a decision was taken to discontinue the petrol engine, but, because orders were still flowing through the system, the last petrol engined version did not go down the assembly line until June 1962. By the spring of 1963 the C and D models were seeing further developments, first with the introduction of a new, fabricated front axle and then with the facility of height control. In October 1965 serial number 317439 rolled down the assembly line, and production of the 850 finally came to an end. In many ways it was a stop-gap measure which could service the market at its smaller end until the 3-cylinder 880 arrived, but in the meantime it was a delightful and highly effective tractor in its own right and 14,242 were produced.

The 850 Implematic was available in either standard or 'Livedrive' form, and the list of standard features was every bit as impressive (and virtually similar) to the 950; these included Implematic hydraulic control; TCU; foot-operated Differential Lock; independent foot and parking brakes; a pto which could operate at 533 rpm on an engine speed of 1,600 rpm; 10-28" rear and 5.50-16" front tyres; 3-point linkage; 2,000lb psi hydraulic pressure; screw-type lift rod and geared levelling lever; front and rear wheel adjustment from 52" to 76"; and, for operator comfort, a de-luxe seat. Optional extras included power steering; 6.00-16" front tyres' 11-28 rear tyres'; high-clearance swinging drawbar; 3-way isolator valve for external hydraulic services; belt pulley unit; a tractormeter which gave land, pto and pulley speeds; overload release and hand clutch; and external lighting. If required the 850 could also be supplied with out a pto and

850 Implematic at David Brown's Wilshaw Farm in 1960

The first Oliver 500 off the line at Meltham Mills

The contrast in sizes between the 850 and 950 models

Seen at Wistaston near Crewe in 1960; an 850 and 950 pose with the 4-ton Garrett steam tractor of 1906 belonging to messrs Hugh and Sam Jackson David Brown dealers

hydraulics as a basic tractor for haulage duties. It was enough to interest the smaller customers all around the world and quite a few big ones as well, including the Oliver Corporation of America. In October 1959 several representatives from this famous tractor manufacturer had been to see the 950 tractor in action, and they were highly impressed with what they had seen. They were to make several successive visits to view the 850, and on one of these occasions my uncle had been given the privilege of taking them to the field-tests in the firms' mini-bus. It seems that they were so impressed with what they had seen 'could hardly contain their excitement on the way back to the works.' A deal was subsequently signed, and Oliver began to market the 850 and the 950 in America, where they were respectively designated as the 500 and 600. Finished in the distinctive green and white livery shown on the rear cover, the first Oliver rolled off the line on Friday 26th February. Our rear picture captures this event, with David Brown junior sitting at the controls of an Oliver 500 (DB850) watched by a group of senior managers from the tractor division. Yet, despite the close tie-in with Oliver's, this in no way affected existing David Brown dealers in either North or South America. The first consignment of 500s and 600s left Meltham station on a special train, hauled by Black Five 4-6-0 No.45101 (P.S., this is an advert to say I write railway books as well). The train of 49 'Oliver' tractors left Meltham on Thursday 10th March for Salford Docks, where they were loaded on to the ss *Manchester Progress* for delivery to Chicago via the St. Lawrence Seaway. In the next few months a further 217 tractors followed the route of these pioneers.

It was good business which would eventually see the combined sales of 2,148 DB-built Oliver tractors. I asked Herbert Ashfield how the deal came about and why it subsequently ended; he writes 'We were looking to sell more tractors in North America and oddly enough we were successful in both Canada and California, but we couldn't get into the Mid-West of the USA where the real big market was. Now, we'd always kept in contact with the American manufacturers but originally they used to sort of laugh at us, we were viewed very much as the poor relations. Then Oliver's suddenly found themselves in trouble with their little machine, they couldn't make it economically enough because they just hadn't got a big enough market. So they began looking at what we were producing, and it must have appealed to them because their Sales Director said "you know we like your little tractor, would you do it in the Oliver livery and let us sell it for you." Obviously we said yes, and designed some cosmetic changes to its appearance and put in a few modifications which they wanted and it did very well. We were still increasing our sales with Oliver when Ford sacked all their franchise dealers in the USA and started supplying tractors through their own distributors, but they were also very short of a small tractor. Accordingly the Ford dealers came to Europe to find a tractor to sell and they chose David Brown, and we couldn't turn down this business as it meant that we had a complete US franchise. So I was sent to Oliver's to tell them we couldn't supply any more tractors – was a hard decision, but nevertheless a commercially correct one.'

Chapter 15
880 Series 1961 - 1965

The 880 Implematic was also introduced in September 1961 and although this model would run concurrently with the 850 until October 1965, it had already been viewed as becoming its natural successor when the 3-cylinder engine became available. At first the 880 appeared with a 4-cylinder engine, and some 12,685 of these were to be built. Yet its greatest success came as the smaller engined version which was introduced in September 1964 and went on to see 39,900 examples of its type. Many people may wonder however, why David Brown thought it practical to run the 850 and 880 at the same time, and this was a question I put to Robin Kedward, a farmer in Monmouthshire who has long worked with the tractor and now become a devoted fan.

'Some farmers wanted a tractor of the same size as the 850, but with increased power, so the 880 was an ideal solution and correctly advertised as the ideal solution for the "one tractor" farm. It was very similar to the 850, but with eight stud wheels (some of the last 850's were eight stud), the tall higher

The first production 880 Implematic

clearance front axle, which was far less prone to wear than the short type used on the 850 and 950, and of course the well proven 42.5 HP engine from the 950 although production of that particular model only continued until December 1962. The 880's were offered with 11/49 (high speed) or 9/50 (low speed) final drives, although I've never seen an 880 with the latter. All the 880 models had bowl-less fuel filters which made servicing easier and the oil

The 880 prototype fitted with experimental loader near Harden Moss

filter was mounted directly onto the cylinder block, dispensing with the aluminium filter head. Also, for the first time I believe, the yellow stove enamelled exhaust was used. This tractor was an immediate success with large and small farmers alike. With its easy starting and economical engine, swinging drawbar and two speed pto. giving superb performance, these little tractors would often out-perform larger models and many spent their working lives driving balers, rotavaters and rotaspreaders.

March 1963 brought the introduction of the fabricated front axle which was fitted first to serial number 355065, and later went on to be used on many other models. The following month saw tractor number 355341 being the first 880 to benefit from the introduction of height control. This very popular tractor remained basically unchanged until the final 4-cylinder 880 rolled off the production line in August 1964, the last one being graced with the serial number 362382. August 1964 also brought dramatic changes in the engine department with the introduction of a new 3-cylinder power unit of a completely new DB design. The AD3/40 series had

Low clearance 880 Implematic with downswept exhaust

(£752.625p). The three-way valve U578 cost £7.5s.0d (£7.25p) and linkage stabilisers at £1-10-0d (£1.50) each. Those were the days!!

Sadly Hunting Pink and Primrose Yellow gave way to Chocolate Brown and Orchid White and in October 1965 the last 880 Implematic to roll off the production line was number 527521. In four years 19,207 880 Implematic tractors were produced, 4-cylinder, 3-cylinder and narrow models, but as many of the narrow models were primarily aimed at the export market, this version of the tractor (like the 850 'Narrow') are very rare indeed. Yet, somewhere around the world careful owners must still be putting these tractors in regular use, as for example one which I spied in a neighbouring field whilst driving down a motorway in Luxembourg in 1996. Robin Kedward testifies to their durability, writing: 'We have had a 3-cylinder model for the last 26 years and not once has it ever let me down! Six months ago I managed to buy a nice 4-cylinder model. It's impossible to say which of these models is the better. I like the quietness and smooth running of the 4-cylinder, but I also like the slogging ability of the 3 cylinder. As for fuel consumption and ease of starting there's nothing between them but I still have a soft spot for my old faithful 3-cylinder!' And no doubt you are not alone Robin!

a cross-flow cylinder head, a bore of 3¹³/₁₆" and a 4¹/₂" stroke and an unusually mounted vertical injection pump. These models were now called the E & F series and commenced with the serial no 521001 in September. My own DB 880 3-cylinder is no 521196, which is one of the very first. Along with the new 3-cylinder engine, which had a much higher torque than the old 4-cylinder, came other changes; for example, the battery was changed to a single 12 volt instead of the two 6's and was now located at the front of the radiator, whilst the air-cleaner was moved from its time honoured position on the left-hand side of the engine to a similar position in front of the radiator. A new type of three-way hydraulic valve was also fitted and after a few months the engine was also fitted with a high-lift camshaft which again improved performance. Plans were already underway for a new model with a much improved hydraulic system (Selectamatic) and this tractor was to be a proving ground for the new 3-cylinder engine.'

With all these new features, plus continual improvements, there is little wonder that the 880 sold so well; yet when we look at the price list for December 1964 we can see another very good reason why farmers would choose it. The price list issued for the Smithfield Show informs us that the 880 Implematic Livedrive with 5.5 - 16 fronts and 12.4/11-28 rears cost just £721.7s.6d (£721.375p) whilst the twelve speed version was a little more expensive at £752-12-6d

880 Implematic with loader adapted for pallet lifting 1965

Chapter 16
990 Series 1961 - 1968

In October 1961, the David Brown Implematic range was improved and upgraded by the introduction of the 990 which, in the years that followed, would prove itself to be one of the best tractors ever to come from the Meltham factory. It was very similar to the 950, but it benefited from a bigger clutch, stronger back-end, heavier castings and a new type of engine with a cross-flow cylinder head. As Robin Kedward writes 'What an engine this turned out to be! It retained the 3" bore of the 950/880, but, with a much longer stroke of 4" " it developed 52.5 BHP at 2200 RPM. It was a power unit that would just laugh at rotaspreaders, wizzlers and forage harvesters. With that extra half inch of stroke this was, in my opinion, an engine with real "guts"- the harder you drove it the better it went. The 990 was sometimes criticised for its slow road speed (same as the 950), but I always thought this was more than made up for with the rest of the gears. No matter what you did with it, the 990 always had the perfect gear for the job.' The matter of gearboxes is continued by Herbert Ashfield, who writes 'The gear-boxes on this new range of tractors were just about as perfect as we could get them, and they were as reliable in service as anything we had made thus far and they really reflected the long tradition of David Brown's gear-making. But

The short and the tall, high and low clearance 990s

the other thing I have to mention is the automatic gearbox, that came in on the 990. Before that we'd done a torque amplifier, which was like a Laycock De-Normanville overdrive on a car, but we did it the other way around. Instead of giving an overdrive, it gave an underdrive. So in effect you got a 2-speed shift automatic, which split your gears; this gave a 12-speed gearbox and you also had a gear that went in-between each gear on

The prototype 990 in 1960

Highway version 990 with loader digger outside Meltham Hall in 1960

A 990 Implematic working in Scandanavia; whilst this volume concentrates on models up to the Implematic range; the Selectamatic models will be more fully covered in Volume Two

the gearbox. This meant that if you were ploughing and the tractor began to pant a bit, you could drop a gear without de-clutching or encountered a sticky patch this would pull you through. Now from that we developed even further, because I realised that if you put two torque amplifiers together, you could get a 4-speed automatic gearbox. We worked on this box, I should think about three or four years before we overcame all the problems because we were in uncharted territory. We required free-wheels and band-brakes and all sorts of odd things of which we had no production experience. Because of this we wanted to be really certain that we'd got all the bugs out, so we held back for quite a while; but when we released it, they put it into production straight away and it performed without any problems. In the field they were so reliable, and very few problems were encountered, I know to this day that there are a lot of them working around here yet.'

The first model to leave the factory was number 440001, and, as with its counterparts, it could have been fitted with either five or six stud front wheels as the six stud front wheels were not yet standard. Two six volt batteries were fitted under the seat, the same as previous models, but the air cleaner was now located in

Export 990s passing Healey House en-route to Hull

front of the radiator. All 990s had six stud rear wheels and were fitted with 11-32 tyres, although 13-28 were an option. This tractor sold like "hot cakes" from the word go and production was soon stepped up to meet demand, and as a result the 950 series was phased out in December 1962. April 1963 soon arrived and along with it came number 453124, now fitted with height control. In August 1963 number 455561 saw the introduction of the fabricated front axle, which was a great improvement on the previous tractors which were all fitted with the tall forged variety.

In August, more dramatic changes were to take place as a single 12 volt battery was now fitted in front of the radiator and the wheel-base lengthened by two inches. So, those who are thinking of restoring a later model 990, beware, the bonnet from an early 950 or 990 will not fit due to it being two inches shorter. A novel feature around this time was the fact that the now redundant battery boxes were fitted with different lids and became tool boxes. Two months later, in October, twelve speed transmission was offered as an option. More minor changes took place in early 1964 and, commencing with tractor number 461120, the glass fuel bowl beneath the fuel tank was dispensed with in favour of a different type of lift-pump and a straightforward push-pull tap. Beginning with number 463764 David Browns began fitting a key-start on the right hand fuel tank support instead of the key and buttons on the left. However, more radical changes were on the way and, in May 1965, the 990 with the tool boxes

beneath the seat disappeared and a new seat and seat support were introduced. Also fitted were different mudguards, which were now bolted directly onto the rear axle and final drives. There was also a different drawbar, pick-up-hitch, three-way valve and the biggest change of all was the rear axle casing. The Selectamatic hydraulic system was obviously on its way and this latest type of axle casing was made in such a way as to facilitate drilling the required holes for this system. However, until such times the holes were blanked, but it was obvious that the castings were being made in readiness for the change and the later Implematic castings even had a blanking plate for the dump valve! Were any of these ever fitted retrospectively with the Selectamatic hydraulic system one wonders?

The Selectamatic was to be a great success, and one which would continue through the years ahead, however by early 1965 things were beginning to change, not least the desire to introduce a new body shape and colour scheme. The advances with the 990 beyond 1965 will be covered in a future volume in this series, but in October 1965 the last 990 Implematic (no.480600) rolled down the line. In just over four years 40,600 990's were produced, including some non-Livedrive and industrial models with twin plate clutches. It was a remarkable record which, at one stage accounted for 50% of the current production at Meltham Mills. The 1964 price list shows the 990 Implematic Livedrive with multi-speed pto. and live dual purpose extra lift hydraulics at the modest sum of £784.9s.0d (£784.45p),

An amazing half-track conversion in Finland which is fitted with a Rottne Timber Crane

and the twelve-speed model at £815.14s.0d (£815.70p). Some of the accessories were priced as follows: Foot throttle U 377 £2.12s.6d (£2.625p); 3-way hydraulic valve U 279 £10.0s.0d; pick-up-hitch U 385 £12.15s.0d (£12.75p) and a quite expensively £54.15s.0d (£54.75p) for power steering. Many farmers came to David Brown for the first time with the 990, and with the company they stayed until Case ended production at Meltham Mills. It was a tractor which bred real customer loyalty, but this loyalty was not easily won and it was satisfaction with the 990 that really put this model head and shoulders above its competitors.

Chapter 17
770 Series 1965 - 1970

We end this book with a brief look at a tractor that is more fully covered in our next work on David Brown Tractors, which covers the period from 1965 onwards. Generally this is known as the 'white era', following the introduction of a new chocolate and orchid white livery which came in with the Selectamatic tractors. However, as the 770 first appeared in the red and yellow livery at the end of 1964, it is fitting to make passing mention of what I consider to be one of the most attractive tractors to come out of Meltham Mills. The genesis of the 770 goes back to the demand for a smaller tractor and was an answer to what some people were looking for in the 2D.

A small tractor was actually built exclusively for the German market between 1962 and 1964, and known as the 750 or U447. This model was produced in a total build quantity of 279 so it hardly forms part of our story, but its concept was important in the later development of the 770. Herbert Ashfield once again retraces the steps of development 'The 750 was just for Germany but they wanted square mudguards, because there many occasions that the whole family would be sat on the tractor. I actually thought that we should put a seat on the mudguards, but we never got around to doing it. But the other thing the Germans wanted was a high-hitch drawbar, even though this would have been condemned as illegal in this country; yet they some way or another got away without turning the tractor over, but as they used a lot of 4-wheeled trailers this probably gave them stability. Their land was mostly flat as well, so if the 750 began to rear up they just put some wheel-weights or some ballast on the front.

The 750 was no use for this country, but we could see that a good small tractor of say 30 to 35 horse-power would take on the requirements of even the smallest users and the 770 was its natural follow up. I seem to remember that we put a 4-cylinder engine in the prototype 770, but when we built them we were on the 3-cylinder 33hp engine with a 3.5" bore. Actually we rapidly got around to putting one of the 3-cylinder engines in the 750s as we were still making these for Germany, and we tested the small engine in this before we came out with it for the 770.' The first production model 770A was launched in January 1965, so it had but nine and a half months in production before the livery was changed. In that short time, however, 1,831 red tractors were built before they went on to the white model which was up-rated to 36 brake horse power. These wonderful little tractors were all that the 2D had promised to be, and much more besides. Their longevity was also remarkable, and after a production run of 10,375 in the white livery, they came to an end in 1970. Yet of these gutsy little tractors, with their 12-forward and 4-reverse gears, at least three are still in regular daily use within a 3-mile radius of the Trans-Pennine offices. Many more have been restored, and of these some wonderfully finished exhibits are presented at shows, rallies and the special events of the David Brown Tractor Club - the only body currently committed to keeping alive the great name of this superlative manufacturer.

Alan Earnshaw